The Sexually Adequate Female

FRANK S. CAPRIO, M.D.

THE CITADEL PRESS—NEW YORK

COPYRIGHT 1953 BY FRANK S. CAPRIO, M.D.
L. C. Card No. 53-11206

All rights reserved. No part of this book may be reproduced in any form without permission in writing from the publisher, except by a reviewer who wishes to quote brief passages in connection with a review.

Illustrations by Josephine Terrill

EIGHTH PAPERBOUND EDITION, MAY, 1963

This is an unaltered and unabridged re-publication of the first edition. Manufactured in the United States of America. Published by The Citadel Press, 222 Park Avenue South, New York 3, N. Y.

To My Sister
JULIE

whose unselfish sacrifices and encouragement made it possible for me to attain a medical education

CONTENTS

	PREFACE	13
1.	WHAT WOMEN SHOULD KNOW ABOUT SEX	17
	The Importance of the Right Attitude	17
	Sex and Health	22
	Infidelity and Sex Incompatibility	25
	Alcoholism and Sexual Frustration	28
2.	WHAT WOMEN SHOULD KNOW ABOUT MEN	32
	Danger Signals for the Unmarried	32
	What Most Men Expect of Women	39
	How to Handle a Neurotic Husband	44
3.	THE MALE AND FEMALE SEXUAL APPARATUS	61
	The Male Sexual Organs and Their Function	61
	The Female Sexual Organs	67
4.	THE ORGASM	74
5.	TYPES OF FRIGIDITY	83
	General Considerations	83
	The Different Kinds of Frigidity	85
	Personality Deviations Associated with Frigidity	91

6. CAUSES OF FRIGIDITY — 100
    Introduction — 100
    Physical Causes — 102
    Sex Ignorance and Prudishness — 103
    Psychic Traumas — 107
    Sex Guilt — 110
    Penis-Envy — 116
    Fears and Complexes — 118
    Masturbation — 124
    Narcissism — 127
    Promiscuity — 128
    Sexual Aberrations — 131
    Bedroom Mistakes
        Faulty Technique — 137
        The Castration Mechanism — 145
    Personality Incompatibility — 149

7. FRIGIDITY AND DREAM ANALYSIS — 154

8. PREVENTION AND TREATMENT OF FRIGIDITY — 168
    The Role of Parents and Society — 168
    Preparing for Marriage
        Sex Education — 171
        Premarital Medical Examination — 173
        Surgical Defloration — 174
    The Ideal Sexual Relationship
        The Right Attitude — 176
        Fore-Play — 177
        The Act of Intercourse — 180
        Variations in Position — 181
        Frequency of Intercourse — 182

	After-Play	184
	Psychotherapy	185
9.	FEMALE HOMOSEXUALITY	188
	Women with Souls of Men	188
	Bisexual Conflicts	207
10.	THE MENOPAUSE	211
	Problems of the Middle-aged	
	The Slackening of Sexual Desire	211
	The Neurotic Spinster	215
	The Repressed Widow	216
	Sex and Love after Fifty	217
	INDEX	221

ILLUSTRATIONS

THE MALE SEXUAL SYSTEM	63
THE MALE SEXUAL APPARATUS	64
THE FEMALE SEXUAL SYSTEM	
External Genitalia	67
Cross Section	68
Internal Reproductive Organs	69

"Women tend to be *frigid* under the conditions of modern civilization, since these conditions involve profound ignorance of sexual matters in both sexes, bad education, prudery and an abnormally late age for the commencement of sexual relationships."

—Havelock Ellis

PREFACE

Approximately seven million American women find sex "physically distasteful or unsatisfactory." One investigator estimates that twenty to thirty percent of women today suffer from FRIGIDITY considered by psychiatrists as a *sexual disorder*—the inability to attain a *vaginal orgasm*. The Kinsey investigation revealed that a third of 8,000 women questioned are partially unresponsive to sex relations and that ten percent of that third are completely unresponsive.

One thing is certain, that the prevalence of this particular sexual disturbance is high enough to account for a large number of divorces (400,000 a year). The majority of these marriage failures are caused by *sexual incompatibility*. Impotence in the male and frigidity among women are the most responsible factors. On the surface it would appear that in-law complications, money difficulties, personality dissensions, and the like, are the main causes for dissolving the marriage. Few would admit to any judge of any court that sexual disharmony was the root-cause of their unhappiness. Many of them are even unaware of or fail to appreciate the relationship of their sex unhappiness to what they claim to be the grounds for the divorce. However, many ministers report that more than half of all the people who come to them for advice are experiencing problems directly related to their sexual functioning.

The high divorce rate is the only one of many consequences of sex incompatibility. Doctors are well aware of the relationships of sexual frustrations to neurotic health complaints among their patients. They know that women who suffer from a lack of sexual response complain of a multiplicity of psychosomatic disturbances such as backaches, chronic headaches, menstrual discomfort, stomach and intestinal disorders, insomnia, nervousness, fatigue, states of depression, as well as many other ailments. The wife who is sexually unsatisfied is usually very difficult to live with. She expresses her frustration in the form of nagging, irritability, temper tantrums, weeping spells, etc. She may try to overcompensate for her thwarted sex life by becoming fanatical about housework, expending her pent-up energy in this way. Many of them not only project their unhappiness onto their husbands but take it out on their children, without being aware of what makes them behave the way they do.

These sexually inadequate women are lonely and develop feelings of hostility toward their husbands whom they often blame for their frigidity. They find that they are unable to tolerate the little things which two people who are sexually compatible would overlook. When a marriage suffers from sexual disharmony it often takes only some minor conflict to bring about the final break. Arguments and disagreements which would normally be quickly settled and forgotten take on major proportions. They are secretly fed and sustained by the virulent hostility that results from a frustrating sexual relationship and poison the marriage. The end result must be either divorce or half-marriage—marriage in name and appearance but not in fact.

I am sure the reader will agree that there exists an urgent need to educate women regarding the facts about this problem. Many women are completely uninformed in these sexual matters while others are misinformed. Just to cite one example, most women harbor the popular concept that frigidity, from its implication, refers to *sexual coldness*. They believe that a woman who is frigid is one who does not desire sex relations and as a consequence cannot enjoy the sex act. This is definitely a fallacy. Frigidity, in its broadest meaning, refers to *sexual inadequacy* among women. A woman can be passionate and still suffer from frigidity.

Frigidity involves the inability to achieve a vaginal orgasm during coitus, also referred to as *orgasm-incapacity*. A wife may even cooperate and make a conscientious effort to experience a climax and fail in her effort. In some instances there is nothing wrong with her sexual desires. The orgasm incapacity is very often caused by sexual incompetence in the male. It is readily understandable how many thoughtless and selfish husbands are capable of causing their wives to "freeze-up" as it were, particularly those who have never mastered the technique of adequate lovemaking.

Most women harbor the popular concept that frigidity refers to sexual coldness. There are many women who do not know that they are frigid. They have no conception of what takes place during an orgasm, and are unable to appreciate the fact that many of their personal problems and chronic unhappiness are caused by a lack of sexual satisfaction.

While many articles have been written on this subject, there have been relatively few books devoted specifically to the problem of frigidity.

It is the purpose of this book (which is a companion volume to my previous work, *The Sexually Adequate Male*,) to examine the scientific facts about this particular sexual disorder in a manner understandable to the layman. It is my hope to convince the reader that practical knowledge concerning the psychological causes of frigidity can help to prevent the development of this condition among women about to enter marriage—that frigidity *can* be cured—that sexual incompetency can be eliminated through education in the principles of sexual harmony—that many marriages can be *saved* and many neurotic wives could reduce their doctor's bills through the attainment of a better adjustment in their physical relations. The sexually adequate woman is a better and happier wife and mother.

FRANK S. CAPRIO, M.D.

Washington, D. C.
June, 1953

1.

WHAT WOMEN SHOULD KNOW ABOUT SEX

The Importance of the Right Attitude

Frigidity may be caused by *faulty attitudes* toward sex. There are many women who have never been educated in sexual matters and do not know what to expect from sex.

There is nothing to be ashamed of in the sexual urge. It is an instinct devised by Nature to promote the propagation of peoples. Had sexual relations not been made pleasureable, the world would have been depopulated long ago. Many young women have been brought up by their elders to think that prudishness is a noble attribute, that extreme modesty is desirable and that sexual contact is something women must endure from their husbands. This is utterly contrary to the design of Nature.

The sexual urge is as natural as the urge to eat. There is this difference, however, between the two impulses: the urge to eat can be controlled for a relatively short time; it must be satisfied. The sexual urge, on the other hand, can be controlled indefinitely. Most unmarried women exert such control. In most instances they are able to do so without struggle; some, however, become neurotics because of the repressed desire which they do not recognize and therefore cannot control.

A young bride has nothing to fear in her sexual relations with her husband. It is a time of lovemaking when the couple within each other's arms become true mates and feel their oneness. It is a part of their married life just as much as sitting down at the table and partaking of the same food, or of sharing their possessions and their pleasure together. It is the taboo-restrictions imposed by society which has made sex appear shameful. At the time of lovemaking hopeful plans are often made and shared together; a time when little misunderstandings are swept away in a mutual love.

It is in this spirit that the woman should share in sex relations with her husband and it is with tender love that the husband should approach his wife. It is when love is omitted that unhappiness begins.

Many women are inadequately prepared for marriage because of sex ignorance. Parents have either been incapable of imparting this necessary knowledge, or they have been squeamishly self-conscious about discussing such matters. Dr. Gillespie, an English psychiatrist, states that the vast majority of neurotic patients whom he interviewed had received no sex instruction from their parents.

Dr. Katherine Davis, author of "Sex Life Of Twenty-two Hundred Women," discovered that the larger percentage of the happily married women had some sex instruction. Many other physicians have stressed the vital importance of the *right attitude* toward sex.

Some women unfortunately harbor false ideas about sex. For example they believe that the only purpose of the sexual urge is to propagate the race, and that passion and sex enjoyment in themselves are unrefined and evidence of lustful or sinful thinking. They believe that a husband should always take the initiative in lovemaking while the wife remains passive; they harbor the misconception that chastity is synonymous with health and that sex compatibility plays only a minor role in marital happiness. Many women feel that the "ideal" courtship is based on platonic love, free of physical lovemaking or stimulation.

Along with these wrong attitudes toward the sex urge is the idea that a sexually maladjusted person will gain happiness through marriage. Marriage is rarely the solution of premarital complexes. On the contrary, the marriage will help to intensify emotional conflicts by making the sex problem more acute. These emotionally upset individuals should get themselves straightened out before entering into a marriage. Otherwise, we can expect such consequences as husbands who are crude, clumsy lovers, wives who are unable or refuse to achieve sexual satisfaction.

"Bad starts" in marriage leave scars that jeopardize chances for sexual happiness in later years. A patient who considered herself hopelessly frigid, discovered upon being reeducated that she possessed an erotic personality that merely needed awakening. Her husband innocently had been cheating her of sexual gratification and had failed to realize it until he learned more about sex technique. He had been a pitiful victim of a premarital, puritanical attitude toward sex and had been unable to free himself of conventional shame and crippling inhibitions. He succeeded in overcoming his shyness and became more positive in his approach.

I do not subscribe to the belief that sex is the principle factor in life, but the confessions of my patients have strongly convinced me that sex is so fundamental that anyone who refuses to discuss sex intelligently or who regards sex as something "dirty" or "ugly" suffers from neurotic hypocrisy.

I recall the case of a patient who actually became nauseated at the thought of having to discuss her sex life in the course of being psychoanalyzed. She had been suffering from headaches, was unmarried and claimed that the subject of sex was repulsive to her. Probing into her background I learned that she had been resorting to self-gratification, and the guilt feeling associated with it caused her to take on this defensive attitude of disgust as a means of camouflaging her sexual transgression. The headaches represented a form of self-punishment, an atonement through suffering for her sense of guilt.

A young woman about to be married can avoid unhappiness that arises from sexual maladjustment by having a premarital check-up and evaluating her *attitude* toward sex. She should possess an adequate knowledge of the facts about sex and appreciate the importance of sex in relation to good health and marital harmony. She should use common sense to guide her in her sex behavior and remember that prudishness, like promiscuity, is the sign of a maladjusted personality. She should be convinced that mutual physical and mental adjustment between partners with an equality of desire produces sexual compatibility—the foundation of a happy marriage.

She should try to find out why and what can be done to improve her sex relations. If she cannot do this without help, she should seek professional advice and assistance.

The right attitude, plus knowledge of the subject—these add up to the best sex adjustment the prospective bride can achieve. Her first step toward that goal is realizing the importance of sex in her life—not as a physical act alone, but an integral part of everything she does.

The way we behave sexually is an expression of our inner personality. It is not a thing apart. It is a powerful force because it is blended inextricably with emotion, with what we call the love-impulse. It has the greatest power for good in our lives when we understand it. It has the greatest power for inflicting suffering if we abuse the physical or neglect the emotional aspect.

A better attitude toward sex means an increased capacity for love and tolerance, a better relationship with family, friends and business associates. It lends an inner poise, a relaxed outlook that is communicated to all around you.

Sex and Health

Women need to realize the important role which sex plays in their physical and mental health. Proof of the neurotic effects of frigidity, for instance, can be found in the records of psychosomatic medicine. The entire medical profession has recognized the fact that many illnesses of the married are due to sexual mismating.

Subconscious sex conflicts send women by the thousands to doctors' offices to find relief from some physical symptom.

I have found from clinical experience that the majority of my neurotic female patients who complained of physical and nervous ailments suffered from some form of sexual maladjustment. To cite an illustration, a married woman, twenty-seven years old, recently was referred to me by her family physician because of her symptoms which consisted of nausea, dizziness, insomnia and headaches. When various medications failed to bring relief, the physician realized that he was dealing with a neurotic.

After several consultations she confessed with great reluctance that she was unable to enjoy sex relations with her husband. Her parents had created in her so great a fear of sex that after marriage she continued to manifest a prudish attitude toward everything pertaining to intimate relations with her husband. Her lack of cooperation, fanatic modesty and fear of childbirth all tended to make her husband extremely unhappy. She boasted of loving him in a "spiritual" way.

Revising her *attitude* toward the marital sexual obligations brought encouraging results. Her neurotic fears disappeared and the readjustment brought happiness to replace her previous bodily complaints.

An unmarried woman, a widow or a divorcee, often tells me, "Doctor, my headaches can't have anything to do with sex. I have no sex life to worry about." She is blind to the realization that her headaches may be nature's way of protesting the lack of balanced living.

Psychiatry has discovered nature's tricks. I tell such patients not to overlook the possibility that there may be a connection between their sickness and their sex life. Whatever sexual conflicts exist must be resolved.

We may go through half a lifetime with a deep maladjustment that is not revealed to us until some physical symptom drives us to a doctor. In most cases, psychosexual maladjustments have had their real start far back in life, in childhood, and have been growing worse for years.

A young lady complained to me of the inability to make friends. She told me that even as a child she had preferred to keep to herself, rather than mingle with the other children of the neighborhood. As she grew older, her self-consciousness increased. She soon developed feelings of inferiority and had no confidence in herself. She developed chronic headaches which became aggravated whenever she attended a social function.

An analysis of her background revealed that her maladjustment was caused by her parents' divorce during her childhood. Her mother was the dominating type and was responsible for enhancing her feelings of inferiority. She warned her against members of the opposite sex, inferring that all men were interested only in sex. Whenever a young man asked her for a date, she was reluctant to accept, as she feared becoming sexually involved. As she became more and more repressed she began to experience tension headaches. It required considerable reeducation for her to appreciate the relationship between her symptoms and psycho-sexual background.

It is this type of background that often leads to the development of frigidity in married life.

Thanks to pioneers like Sigmund Freud and Wilhelm Stekel, who proved the close relationship between sex and health, we are alert to the need for enlightenment. Enlightenment means the end of much unnecessary suffering. Now we have many doctors writing books, articles and pamphlets on the relation of sex to health.

Before the growth of this discovery of the importance of sex to health, all schools recognized the need for gymnastics, fresh air periods and sports to develop good physical health. Now we know that in addition to physical exercise, we need an understanding of our emotions, our sex life, and how to achieve good mental health. Eventually, no education will be considered complete without sex instruction which can be incorporated in courses dealing with mental hygiene. We are only witnessing the beginning.

Fortunately, you do not have to wait until universal sex education is an accomplished fact. As an individual, you can start your own education in sex health which you did not get from school or your parents. Understanding this aspect of your life will mean that for the rest of your years, you can enjoy better health and better living.

Infidelity and Sex Incompatibility

The predisposition to infidelity, in some instances, lies in the individual character make-up long before the person marries. Some women are more prone to infidelity situations than others.

Infidelity is more likely to occur among sexually unsatisfied women. The sexually satisfied woman has little cause to become involved in extra marital relations.

Frigid wives often become *unfaithful* because they hope to find their ideal sexual partner.

Several years ago, a couple consulted me because of their marital difficulties. They had been married three and a half years and the wife complained that she had never experienced a sexual climax at any time with her husband.

She had come to the conclusion that her husband was responsible for the sex incompatibility—that his technique was inadequate. Upon questioning the husband, I learned that he had considerable premarital sexual experience and no woman had ever complained before of his technique. He further informed me that his wife showed very little response to preliminary lovemaking, found it difficult to concentrate during the sex act, and despite his efforts to prolong the act, she was unable to attain an orgasm.

During my interviews with the wife I learned that she had experimented by indulging in extramarital affairs in an effort to prove to herself that her husband was at fault. But instead, she learned that she was incapable of achieving an orgasm despite the change in sexual partners. Her husband was unaware that she had been unfaithful. She realized that her husband was not to blame and was anxious to learn the cause of her frigidity.

The analysis revealed that she had been extremely narcissistic and as an adult she attracted much attention by her beauty. When it came to having sex relations with her husband, she was more interested in being complimented and praised and was unable to concentrate on the physical sensations of the sexual act. Her self-love was so excessive that she could only think of her hair being disheveled, or her make-up smeared during intercourse.

Most important of all, she learned that the sex incompatibility was caused by her own frigidity, which in turn had caused her to try other sexual partners only to learn that infidelity was no solution to her problem.

In some instances a wife who is frigid in an unhappy marriage may be denied sex by a sadistic or impotent husband. She turns to infidelity for a solution. Infidelity in such a case may bring about the dissolution of a hopeless marriage that has been dragging on for years. It is not the wisest method, but one that is undertaken in a desperate effort to solve one's problem.

Almost every case of unfaithfulness involves sexual intimacy. There are very few platonic infidelities in which a husband or wife trysts clandestinely for the sake of friendship only. Because infidelity involves a problem in sex behavior, it comes—or should come—within the psychiatrist's field.

To the psychiatrist sexual cheating—like other behavior deviations—is neither to be condemned nor condoned. In the case of alcoholism, we try to correct the practice of drinking oneself blind because it never solves anything. We don't condemn the person prey to the bad habit—we treat the underlying cause. It is the same with infidelity.

I never recommend or prescribe infidelity as a cure for frigidity. I never tell a patient, "What you need is a love affair—go out and get a new sex partner." I tell my patients that infidelity is not a solution to a stalemated marriage and may lead to worse complications. It can have consequences wholly unforeseen by the person who starts with what she may believe to be one isolated instance of unfaithfulness. It often becomes linked with secondary addictions. Infidelity is frequently paired with alcoholism. The highball and the sleeping pill are common sedatives for a guilty conscience.

Repeated infidelity by a wife is never going to improve her husband's sex technique. Her only course is to give him a chance to improve himself and become a good sexual partner to her.

To repeat, adultery is no solution to the problem of frigidity. Society is handling the problem of infidelity on the basis of its moral aspect alone. It needs to be studied as a *psychiatric* problem in *behavior-deviation* common to women who are sexually unsatisfied. These women must be made to understand the causes of their infidelity and be given practical steps to take in recovery.

Alcoholism and Sexual Frustration

With few exceptions, people who drink to excess are sexually maladjusted. In my own experience, I have yet to treat a woman with a drinking problem who did not have an accompanying sexual problem. The sexual frustration may arise out of the repression of the sexual urge, or it may involve a promiscuity complex, infidelity, homosexuality, or frigidity.

A frigid woman may want to engage in an extramarital

affair, but because of her feelings of guilt is compelled to drink to excess in order to drown out her conscience. She wants her pleasure without guilt and under the influence of alcohol she is not responsible for her behavior.

Many women feel that they are less inhibited under the influence of alcohol and are more apt to achieve a sexual climax after several drinks. This is true of both sexes, provided the amount of drinking is limited to a few drinks. But when the drinking becomes excessive, it makes the man more impotent and the woman more frigid. She becomes aware that she is intoxicated, makes herself less attractive, feels ashamed and often converts the lovemaking into a fiasco.

The wife of a successful engineer consulted me because of her compulsion to drink to excess. She stated that her husband, while he gave her material comforts, failed to satisfy her sexually. She described him as being awkward and a clumsy lover. Because of her sexual frustrations she began to drink excessively and became promiscuous. While she achieved an orgasm in some instances, in the course of her extramarital contacts, most of the time she was frigid. She further complicated her sex life by indulging in masturbation during intervals of intercourse with her husband. In this particular case the husband was encouraged to avail himself of psychiatric treatment. Upon improving his technique his wife found her sex life more satisfactory. She succeeded in limiting her drinking and decided to give up her clandestine relations with other men.

In another instance, a husband came to me for help, claiming that his wife drank to excess only on week ends. She held a very good position and always managed to get a very high efficiency rating for her work. But when she came home on a Friday evening she would begin drinking beer to excess and continue drinking over the week end only to sober up for work on Monday morning. When I questioned the husband about their sex life, he told me that his wife was frigid. He regarded himself as an adequate lover. His wife had frankly admitted having had sex relations with other men prior to marriage but she had never achieved an orgasm during intercourse. After several sessions with the wife I learned that she had masturbated to excess during childhood and had continued the practice even after marriage. The guilt which she experienced from masturbating and the frustration of not being able to attain an orgasm during sex relations with her husband turned her to drink.

She responded to treatment favorably, succeeded in controlling her urge to masturbate, developed insight into the cause of her frigidity and when she began having vaginal orgasms during coitus, she had no further desire for alcohol.

There are endless case illustrations showing the relationship of sexual frustrations to problem-drinking among women. However, the various individual cases almost parallel each other. The alcohol is used as a means of escaping the awareness of their sexual difficulty. While it may seem to lessen the guilt feelings *temporarily*, it actually increases the feelings of guilt, making for even greater sexual frustration. This in turn causes the person to resort to more alcohol to drown the increased guilt.

Our records show that the majority of women who drink to excess are frigid. When the frigidity is cured the need for excessive alcohol is eliminated.

2.

WHAT WOMEN SHOULD KNOW ABOUT MEN

Danger Signals for the Unmarried

It is true that love is not always rational. When people fall in love their better judgment does not enter too often into the picture. It is also true that neither the love relationship nor the marriage relationship can operate on a slide-rule formula basis.

Nevertheless, keeping in mind that love is irrational and that there is no ready-made formula, one can benefit by certain guiding principles in choosing a mate.

Many women are sexually unsatisfied only because they marry highly neurotic men. It is during courtship that one should learn to recognize those character traits in men which inevitably lead to marital difficulties later on.

Here are a few personality liabilities which often show up during courtship that may be regarded as danger signals. Incidentally, I do not wish to convey the impression that men who exhibit any of the following traits are hopeless. They merely represent symptoms of some underlying neurosis that requires psychiatric treatment. Women must not be deceived into thinking that marriage alone will cure these men of their undesirable neurotic personality traits. If they are going to change for the better, they must show evidence of it prior to marriage and must not be too proud to seek professional assistance if the neurosis is a deep-seated one.

1. Alcoholism. The man who drinks to excess suffers from a serious personality maladjustment. The fact that a man is able to earn a good living despite his drinking doesn't make him eligible for marriage. A prudent woman will give her man the alcohol test before she commits herself. If she suspects that he is more than a "social drinker," she saves herself a lifetime of grief by putting thumbs down on the proposal. It's not worth the gamble. Inebriates belong to the unmarriageable group. They tend to make alcoholics of their wives. It is best to be cautious when a suitor promises to give up drinking after the wedding ceremony. Many women flatter themselves by thinking that they have reformed a "Lost Week-End" lover and that his case is an exception to the rule, where a weakness for alcohol is concerned. All too soon after the honeymoon the husband slips back into his drinking habits.

There is nothing so intolerable as to have an alcoholi·

husband on your hands. Drinking has wrecked many a marriage. You can either play safe by marrying a non-drinker or someone who is no more than a social drinker, or risk consequences if your guess was wrong about his promise to give up drinking.

Many alcoholic husbands suffer from some form of impotence and often leave their wives *sexually unsatisfied*.

2. *Don Juanism*. When you discover your prospective husband indiscreetly goes out with many women it may be better to invest your life's future in a partnership that's more reliable.

Only recently a sexually dissatisfied married woman told me, between sobs, of her husband's weakness for other women. "I can't understand why my husband likes to torture me by confessing that he goes out with the blonde in his office. He is forever telling me he can't help himself because she's attractive."

"Did your husband have these Don Juan tendencies before you married him?" I asked.

"Yes, doctor, in fact he thought it was perfectly legitimate to continue going out with his other girl friends even after we were engaged to be married."

"Then, why did you marry him?" I asked.

"I thought surely after our marriage he would settle down," she replied. "I suppose too it was because he was a handsome man and I felt flattered that he had paid any attention to me at all."

It was her self-confessed feelings of inferiority that made

her blind to the price it cost her for marrying an attractive "wolf" whose appetite she could never satisfy.

Therefore, if you feel your engaged partner has a Don Juan complex, judging from his past record, it would be best to take serious thought before you express that final commitment—"I do."

There are too many broken-hearted and *sexually dissatisfied wives* who lead empty lives because of their error in judgment during courtship.

3. *Family Slaves.* Living close to one's parents invites in-law complications, a serious threat to marital happiness. There are many men who cannot make up their minds whether to marry and break away from home, or remain single, preferring mother's over solicitousness and tender concern for their welfare.

Any display of excess attachment to one's family should be a warning sign. It means marrying someone who will try to be half-husband and half-son, only to make a bad job of both. Grownups who are unable to sever unhealthy family ties are not quite ready for marriage.

If they do marry, trouble is just around the corner, ready to pop out. Usually such persons manifest extreme possessiveness and become jealous at the first sign of any displacement of affection.

4. *Jealousy.* No wife wants to spend her married life having to explain why she danced a second time with a certain man, or have to account for every minute of her time spent away from home.

Men who are unreasonably jealous generally suffer either from a feeling of insecurity or they feel guilty because of their own repressed desires to commit adultery.

I'm speaking, of course, of unjustified jealousy. One usually finds jealousy existing in a man who is courting an exceptionally attractive woman.

I have also found from experience that wives who consult me because of their husband's abnormal jealousy, describe the husband as being *sexually inadequate* (another warning for those in love with victims of a jealousy complex).

It is a serious misconception to conclude that jealousy is a sign of true love. On the contrary, it may indicate that the person wishes to marry from a neurotic motive—to overpossess the other person for physical gratification only, to desire love instead of giving it.

5. *Gambling.* The man who occasionally bets at the races during his winter vacation to Florida, or enjoys an occasional game of poker and plays for stakes that damages no one's pocketbook would not come under the classification of being a gambler. A gambler is a person who either engages in illicit gambling, risking getting into difficulty with the law, or a man who makes gambling, whatever form it takes, a major thing in his life. He is driven by a compulsion to win all or lose all. He never knows when to stop. One week he lives in luxury and the next he borrows money to return to the race track. His character is as unstable as his luck. He becomes irritable when he loses and takes it

out on the world. Psychoanalysts have concluded that men with a gambling mania are basically unhappy and maladjusted. Some of them are sexually impotent and try to seek thrills through gambling as a substitute for their difficulty to enjoy sex relations with a woman. Those who do satisfy women sexually do so mechanically, without any expression of love for their partner. They are too preoccupied with their neurotic love of gambling to have developed a normal love for a woman. A woman who is courted by a man who spends most of his evenings with the boys playing cards until early hours of the morning, should think carefully before marrying him. It is doubtful whether she will ever feel secure in a marriage to a man of this kind.

I have treated a good many women who complained of being frigid who were married to gamblers. The husband would come in at 4 A.M. in a grouchy mood, confessing that he had lost several hundred dollars and expecting the wife to gratify his sexual needs. It is understandable how a wife in such a situation would find sex unattractive, and find it difficult to achieve an orgasm during intercourse.

It is definitely established that habitual gambling is the symptom of a maladjusted or neurotic personality.

6. Sex Complexes. In talking to a man about sex, you can soon learn if he harbors normal or neurotic attitudes toward that which is essential to his happiness in marriage. No one is adequately prepared for marriage unless he possesses a reasonable amount of sex education. I insist that my unmarried patients read at least two or three authoritative books on the subject. It is because of premarital sexual ignorance that we find women married to impotent men, and suffering nervous breakdowns as a consequence; or men married to frigid wives with resultant excuses for extramarital relations.

Marriage is no solution to one's sexual conflicts. Those who suspect they are sexually inadequate should not marry until they have been cured of their particular sexual disorders.

The woman who minimizes the role that sex harmony plays in marriage is potentially a bad matrimonial risk. Likewise, a man who is abnormally inhibited and behaves as though he were courting his sister often turns out to be a clumsy lover. His inadequacy becomes the source of much grief.

A patient told me she was afraid to marry a certain young man who had proposed. She had been going with him for three years and he behaved so much like a perfect gentleman (never having made an attempt to kiss her) that she began to wonder if he knew the "facts of life."

It is alarming to discover after marriage that your husband prefers to sleep in a separate bedroom, particularly when you realize that sexual deprivation can lead to neurotic illness.

7. *Neuroticism.* Neurotic men as a rule make bad marriage partners. They usually complain a lot, are health-conscious and are continually going to doctors for different colored pills. Constant dissatisfaction is another symptom.

The most predominant characteristic is their chronic unhappiness. An unhappy man needs to see a psychiatrist before venturing into marriage.

It is best to think twice about walking to the altar with a man who becomes frequently depressed, who enjoys criticizing everyone and everything, who suffers from exaggerated ailments and who frequently displays an ugly disposition by becoming abusive, angry and argumentative. You assume a heavy liability when you risk marriage to a man of this type.

If you are in doubt about yourself and your partner, consult a marriage counselor. At least he will see to it that your heart doesn't rule your mind. Perhaps some day all engaged couples, instead of the present-day few, will be able to go to a marriage clinic where they can determine if they are properly suited to each other. It will mean fewer divorces and fewer neurotic children.

What Most Men Expect of Women

Sexual compatibility is dependent upon personality compatibility. Many husbands claim they no longer love their wives and have little desire to have sex relations with them. Infrequency of sex relations is the first symptom of marital incompatibility. Sexual deprivation in turn results in the development of *frigidity* among many women. A woman will often tell her psychiatrist:

"We have sex so infrequently, I no longer have any feelings about it. It doesn't bother me any more. I could live the rest of my marriage without it."

This state of affairs usually results from a husband and wife not understanding each other and making no attempt to improve the situation. They go from sleeping in a double bed to twin beds to separate rooms to the husband spending an occasional night at the club.

I tell such couples that to keep love alive there must be *harmonious* living—a blending of their hearts and minds. Bickering and quarreling have no place in an ideal relationship. Much of this personality incompatibility is brought on by a failure of the respective sexes to appreciate each other's needs.

The husband argues: "I can't understand my wife. Nothing I do pleases her. She is always complaining about something."

The wife protests: "If my husband would only be considerate and try to understand the situation from a woman's point of view, we would get along much better. He's so immature at times, I wonder if he'll ever grow up." And there you have it—a typical "stalemate."

While it is true there are men who are short, others tall; some slender, others fat; those who are educated in contrast to those less educated; some religious, others irreligious; the few who are normal, the many who are neurotic; one can safely arrive at some common denominators that apply to all men irrespective of color of skin or nationality.

The majority may feel they belong to the *important* sex—that it's a man's world. Hence he is to be respected merely for being a man. This contention that the world and its problems belong to the male species impresses me as an unwarranted presumption. The universe manifestly was created for women as well as men. The treasures and pleasures of the world are bestowed upon both sexes.

Women should remind themselves that the *average* man enjoys having his ego inflated. The ego may be likened to the skeletal structure of the body. Without it we would be unable to stand erect or walk. Every man possesses a *mental* skeleton—his ego. When it collapses everything suffers. He must be made to *want* to work, to *want* to succeed, to *want* to love. A wise wife will remind herself to constantly *encourage* her husband. Men need to be *inspired*. It's the very thing they frequently find in the "other woman"—ego inflation.

Today's husband expects his wife to be a companion—one who shares in his interests. A wise woman will take an interest in her husband's job or profession. She will work with him and not against him. She realizes that his future is her future. She will grow with him and manifest an appreciation of the better things in life. Many husbands complain that their wives are unable to participate in an intelligent conversation and that they have no desire to improve themselves. They accuse them of being intellectually lazy, that they don't find it important to make time for a cultural interest or recreational hobby. They are always finding excuses—they have no time for reading or for anything else.

Now, what does all this have to do with the problem of sexual frigidity? The relationship becomes clear when we realize that these are the very women who are unable to make their married life interesting, are bored with the monotony of household drudgery, who are too tired to enjoy sex relations. Self-dissatisfaction invariably leads to sexual dissatisfaction.

An unhappy wife, whether the unhappiness comes from within or from living with a neurotic husband, in all probability will suffer from frigidity. Many a wife has turned against sex because she has been disillusioned by a husband who abuses her. Others are sexually unresponsive because of their own personality deficiencies. I have encountered a large number of women who have said:

"Doctor, the fault lies with me. I have a wonderful husband. He's kind and understanding and is very tender and considerate when he makes love to me. You see I come from an unhappy home. My parents separated. I never knew what it was to be happy. Whenever anyone is kind to me, I envy them. My husband should have married someone else. I'm a millstone around his neck. I hate myself for it. It's not fair that I should make him so unhappy."

Husbands don't react well to this kind of inner unhappiness. Some take it until they reach a point of saturation and then decide to divorce the wife who refuses to "change" or to go to someone to help her "change."

A man expects a wife to keep herself *detached* from the

unhappiness of her family. He wants her to forget the past and concentrate on the present and future. Some women, however, aren't happy unless they're unhappy. They always have to have something to complain about.

Excessive complaining is *fatal* to a happy marriage. I have witnessed the dissolution of many marriages because the wife never seemed to be satisfied. Constant fussing, bickering, and nagging will only result in a chain of undesirable consequences—personality incompatibility, sex incompatibility, divorce and lonesomeness.

Men aren't looking for *competitors*. They want someone who will *cooperate,* who will *listen,* who will express an opinion in the form of a helpful suggestion. A wife can maintain her individuality, have a thinking brain of her own and still know how to advise her husband without his feeling that she wants to wear the pants. Men like clever women. They don't want to be married to "hysterics"— women who become emotional, are oversensitive and weep at the slightest provocation.

As for a sexual partner, men prefer a wife who is aggressive sexually after he has once initiated the advances. The woman who exhibits undue shyness, wants the lights out, and is afraid to manifest evidence of being aroused is unattractive to most men. When the wife behaves in bed as she thinks the "other woman" would behave she is less likely to lose her husband. It is one of her duties not only to learn something about preparing appetizing meals, but she should also learn how to *satisfy her husband sexually* which in turn will result in her own greater happiness. In England the marriage ceremony contains the phrase, "With my body I thee worship." It might be well if more women in this country made full use of its implication.

This advice applies to wives who are married to men whose sexual technique is adequate. A man who is a good provider, considerate, kind and a good lover doesn't deserve to be "castrated" in bed by a wife who is neurotically prudish and sexually unresponsive. Such a wife in all fairness to herself and her husband should seek professional assistance to overcome the cause of her frigidity.

If the wife *is* sexually responsive, has a normal disposition, and has done everything in her power to cooperate toward making the marriage a success, but her husband is sexually inadequate, inconsiderate and abusive, then she needs the kind of advice given in the following section.

How to handle a Neurotic Husband

The first step in the proper handling of a neurotic husband is to be able to recognize his neuroticism and become convinced that it represents the symptom-expression of some underlying personality disorder. It will also enable the wife to appreciate why she is unable to respond to him sexually.

There are many types of neurotic husbands. There is the kind who is egotistical, self-centered and demanding. His wife is expected to conform to all of his plans. He marries for convenience, for the gratification of his hunger and sex instincts. He likes to bully his wife, gives vent to outbursts of profanity and anger and thinks a woman's activities should be confined to the kitchen and bedroom of her home. He may be an introvert living in a private world of his own, surrounded by an invisible wall. If he is an extrovert, he monopolizes the conversation and becomes the know-it-all type. He may marry a beautiful woman only to feed his vanity—to have his friends remark about her beauty.

He enjoys flirtations with women who inflate his ego, but he fails to give his wife the attention and affection she needs. If he engages in a quarrel, he is always right. Company bores him. His selfishness is manifested in his desire to be loved and respected without doing any loving himself.

The introverted egoist's nerves are upset by little frustrations. He believes in a European master-slave relationship. If he slips and philanders he expects to be forgiven and rationalizes his infidelity with some flimsy excuse. But should his wife make some innocent gesture of affection toward a friend at a party, he becomes insanely jealous. He understands little about a woman's emotions. If he happens to be handsome his conceit becomes intolerable. If he's a "big shot" in business, politics, or his profession, he expects to be treated like a "big shot" at home. In a marriage to a neurotic husband of this kind, the romance can end with the wedding ceremony.

Not many neurotic husbands are so unfortunate as to have all of these bad qualities but if a man has a large percentage of them, it is high time for an overhauling of his personality before he becomes too unbearable.

Then there is the spoiled-child type of neurotic husband. The marriage represents a child-mother relationship. He is dependent and has never been able to detach himself from his mother's apron strings. Psychiatrists use the term "adult infantilism" to describe his childlike behavior. He is usually shy and fears responsibility. In many instances he is an only child—the product of an indifferent father and an over-indulgent mother. He is extremely sensitive, prone to sulk and pout when his feelings have been hurt. When he is sick in bed, he requires a lot of attention and "motherly" affection.

In his lovemaking he is clumsy or inadequate or may be suffering from a sexual disorder of some kind. He either overindulges his wife at inappropriate times, or goes to the other extreme and becomes sexually uninterested. When he becomes angry he behaves like a spoiled child and makes himself obnoxious. His attempt to appear "masculine" makes him ridiculous.

Emotionally he is possessive and jealous. He is sentimental and a family slave in the sense that he is still comparing his wife to his mother and to his sister. His immaturity and emotional instability makes him a problem for any wife. He prides himself in having been the "white" sheep of his family—the noble type. Usually he covers up a strong inferiority complex for which he overcompensates. The wife finds herself married to an infant adult.

The husband who is a neurotic extrovert is the person who seeks his happiness entirely outside himself. He must always be doing something or being something. He becomes a show-off, trying to exhibit his superior skill in his work and in his pleasure. His pride in his wife's and children's accomplishment is boastful and excessive. He is restless, always seeking excitement; always attempting something new. His superiority becomes too evident.

This husband's desire to excel, to be admired and envied, stems from an inner realization that he stands on a false pedestal and he fears that someday he may fall off. The drive within him arising from this feeling of inadequacy causes him to run from himself, to lose himself among his friends and emerge as their leader. When, however, his neuroticism extends to domination in his home, his wife, unless she "plays along" in order to hold the family intact, may enter the divorce courts charging "mental cruelty."

The introvert, neurotic husband is a little easier to get along with but less exciting and interesting. He lives within himself, retreats to his books and his hobbies, shunning outside interests. It is when his interest in self begins to shut out his wife and family that this marriage, too, becomes brittle.

Another type of neurotic husband is the one with the mother complex. His mother has been a "Mom." Unhappy in her own marriage (or perhaps a widow), she diverts her possessive love to her son. She plays up to him to win his complete devotion. She becomes the "best little mother in the world." His marriage can be successful only if he marries a woman of his mother's type—this often occurs—and if his wife is willing to accept a secondary role. His mother is the head of the family, if she is still living. Even if she has gone or is living at a distance, his life and his reactions are turned to her ideas. If his mother is dead, his wife has to assume the mother role. He is one of her children and she must treat him as the spoiled one, indulging his every wish, living her life unselfishly so that his happiness can be complete. She seldom succeeds in satisfying him because she cannot reach the ideal he has set up—his mother. Often there are no children in this family, for this husband denies all amorous feeling for his "Mom" and therefore for his wife. He is more than likely to be unfaithful, seeking his sexual satisfactions elsewhere.

The jealous, possessive, neurotic husband is much too common. His wife is his property, she "belongs" to him. He is jealous of her friends, male and female. He demands her entire interest and devotion. He rages if she is politely pleasant to another man and accuses her of infidelities. Usually he mistrusts her because he is untrustworthy himself. All the sins of which he accuses her he commits himself, actually, or in his erotic dreams. Many wives, loving their husbands, have had to separate from them because of the insane jealousy publicly and privately expressed. The papers daily report murders by these husbands whose jealous beliefs regarding their wives have been entirely groundless. It is only by revealing to husbands the true reasons behind their jealousy and the ridiculousness of their suspicions, that the sexual love of the husband can be turned into normal channels.

Another common type of neurotic husband is the middle-aged philanderer. True, many a husband strays long before he reaches middle-age but usually these marriages break up early. The man who has reached the male change-of-life, whose sexual activities begin to lag, suddenly is seized with a desire to appear young and virile again. He capers coltlike before other women and he begins to pay attention to those younger than his wife. The younger woman's response to his attentions flatters and inflames his faltering sexual abilities. There is always some woman with thwarted sex desires ready to pounce upon a straying Lothario. His new love may run him a merry race and as merrily toss him aside. Desiring a home and security, she may marry him when he secures a divorce from his outraged wife. He thinks he is enjoying a renewed youth and consents to a constant round of cocktail parties, night clubs and week-end bouts. His virility delights him—for a time. Soon his age and perhaps prostatic trouble catch up with him. He begins to long for the old fireside-slippers-pipe era, someone to cater to his pleasures and his comforts, nursing him in his illnesses, worrying about him. He wants to be the important loved one of the household.

These marriages can be saved if husband and wife can

be made to understand the origin of the neuroses in the various types of neurotic husbands, and make an honest effort mutually to work together to overcome the repressed desires that lead to neurotic behavior.

There are specific ways of handling a neurotic husband—ways that will not only help him, but will save wear and tear on the nerves of the wife who has to live with him. The important first step is to be *tolerant*.

One reason a psychiatrist can deal successfully with a neurotic husband when his wife cannot is because the psychiatrist is patient and tolerant with him. He bears in mind that all neurotic husbands are *unconsciously* motivated. Their irritating acts are not deliberately thought out but are compulsive. They are compelled by pressures within to act as they do. The difficult or neurotic husband invariably feels deep inside himself that he is unloved, rejected. In many ways, he is like a wayward child who has tantrums without quite knowing why. Understanding the cause of the tantrums will not make them easier to bear, but it will help you to deal sensibly with his outbursts.

The neurotic husband who is difficult is often lovable in many ways. Too frequently, however, his good traits are overshadowed by his exasperating ones, until finally all his good characteristics are lost sight of. A wife may say in despair of her neurotic husband, "Oh, I can't stand him—he's killing me." From that point on, she is too busy hating him even to try to understand him.

The neurotic husband needs exactly what most wives fail

to give him. He needs a positive, not a negative, approach. He needs to be told what's right with him as well as what's wrong. You can't fool him with a trumped-up pep talk you don't mean. He is sensitive to hostility and insincerity.

The second step is to *face the facts.* Don't rail at an unfortunate situation; study it. This is especially essential in marriage. Face the fact that your husband is what he is —that he is *neurotic,* and give up the ghost ideal that haunts your marriage. We all have a ghost ideal when we marry, and some of us spend an unhappy lifetime trying to change the human being we married into that ideal.

The complaint I hear most often about the hard-to-live-with husband is, "But, Doctor, he's so unreasonable! He never sees any point of view but his own."

This is perfectly true. The neurotic husband doesn't answer an argument reasonably because he is not thinking— he's emoting. He is defending. He is protecting his thin-skinned sensitivity from what he feels is a hostile attack.

The thinking of this kind of neurotic husband is turned inward. "How does it affect me?" is his major concern when faced with a problem. The reason for his self-concern is fear. Somewhere along the line, the neurotic husband has become convinced that he's not getting the love and attention he needs. He craves it, and he doesn't know how to get it—he is in fact, ashamed of his need and often refuses to recognize it consciously. So he develops a grievance against the world for failing to appreciate him.

This aggrieved feeling finds its outlets. The man who

feels he's being passed over at his job, for instance, gives vent to his suffering ego at home.

Such a case was the subject of a play not too long ago. Frederic March played the role of a clerk of small means who had completely lost hope of advancement. He loved his wife and daughter, but coming home to them was only a bitter reminder of how poorly he was able to provide. So he blew up in furious irritation at the smallest item on the grocery or telephone bill, made life very unpleasant for his wife, his daughter, the cat.

His angry outbursts seemed to be evidences of ill temper, but actually, they were cries of fear and disappointment at his own inability to cope with life. A hard man to live with? Yes, but fortunately in his case, his wife never lost sight of his lovable qualities and dogged efforts—and together they turned even the loss of his precariously held job into a moral triumph for his hurt pride.

The neurotic husband who feels inadequate may drive himself and his family into a frenzy in his determination to push himself ahead in his work with the aim of winning attention. Or he may turn to escape—through alcohol or flirtations, or a hobby that will absorb him so completely he can't think about his humiliating standstill at work.

He may take refuge from a hostile world in sickness and turn his grievance into hypochondria. This, he will not do deliberately but he may drift gradually and unconsciously into the comforting excuse.

With his eyes fixed only on his own failure or his fear

of it—the neurotic husband sees all his problems practically insurmountable, but all yours as trivial. In fact, he doesn't recognize yours as problems at all.

Many a wife has talked herself hoarse trying to convince her neurotic husband that having him home on time to eat dinner is as important to her as that extra half-hour at the office is to him. But at the end of her argument, her husband can simply point out that she's nagging and that it's no fun to come home to a nagging wife after a day's work. And the rankling injustice of his attitude is made only more painful by the grain of truth in what he says.

The wife in such a case is dealing ineffectually with the situation, and as a healthy-minded person she should instinctively recognize that fact. A neurotic husband too out of balance to show a fair consideration for his wife and her work role is not adjusted to reality, and probably is a sick person. He literally doesn't dare admit any arguments for her side of the case—for if he does, his whole protective house of cards topples.

The wife of the too jovial social drinker, the wife of the perennially roving eye, the wife of the silent devotee of a hobby, the wife of the habitual gambler—are all wasting their breath in tirades. If they find themselves married to husbands with such nervous compulsions, from nail-biting to drinking, argument gets them nowhere. It is as useless as trying to argue a person out of an attack of migraine.

Never *argue* with a neurotic husband. It is a very important rule. Discuss a problem calmly, yes, but if things have reached such an acute stage that mere mention of the sore subject provokes argument, then drop it. Give the neurotic husband a long enough cooling-off period so that he can calmly discuss the subject when it arises again.

I am at present trying to help several women whose lives are being made miserable by husbands so absorbed in their hobbies or their food and comfort that their wives have no companionship of any kind. These men live at an infantile level, shrinking from normal social life. They come home to hobby or radio or television—and ignore their wives, for the most part.

One woman told me her husband has not taken her out in five years. And he won't have anyone in. He's too uncomfortable. He sits in his easy chair all evening, has a snack beside him at the television set and never opens his mouth, except to put the food in.

Neurotic husbands, such as this one, are trying to make mothers of their wives. No doubt they have been coddled as sons, and the world hasn't shown them Mama's loving appreciation. They substitute childish oral satisfaction in food or pipe for a normal marital relationship. The fact that their wives may have worked all day, put the children to bed, and prepared a nice dinner doesn't bring a word of thanks from such neurotic men as these. Day in and day out, they may not even talk to their wives. Many of them leave their wives *sexually unsatisfied.*

I emphasize this type of thing because I encounter it so often. The more I see of marriage, the more I realize how little men understand their wives emotionally. They just don't seem to know how women feel or what they need. As a result more and more disillusioned women are getting divorces. In many of these cases, the wife would do better to put her skill to work educating her present husband. For the chances are that she will run up against similar quirks in the next one.

I am convinced that in almost every case it is the woman who makes or breaks the marriage. In general, women make few demands of marriage—they are content with their homes for the most part, and as long as the man is halfway human, they'll go along with him through good times and bad.

But the times being what they are, men are increasingly prone to neurotic strain. Women need to know how to cope with men who may be fairly good husbands in many respects, but who are nearly impossible to live with in certain ways.

The wife of the self-absorbed, neurotic husband has to wake him up to the fact that she is an individual. She should let him know that she is his wife, not a coddling substitute for Mama. Not by nagging him will she change his ways; the more she scolds him, the more grimly will he hold on to what he feels is his threatened independence. He will only feel more certain that he is completely misunderstood.

Instead of wearing herself out in fruitless resentment, the wife of such a neurotic husband has resolutely to set about filling her own time in the evenings. She must develop a cheerful unconcern about how her husband spends his. At first, it may be all pretense; everybody has to be something of an actor in this world. There are times when it is better to pretend a little—to act a role stronger than you may feel, until you grow into it.

The wife's asserting her individuality is also effective treatment for the husband overaddicted to a hobby. With the pressure of censure removed, such a man will eventually poke his head cautiously from behind his citadel of paper or hobby—noting the absence of the familiar concern or scolding. He will miss his wife's actual presence, if she busies herself in some constructive activity of her own. And he will become increasingly amenable to reason as his thinking begins to turn outward.

Even if the cure is not one hundred percent, the wife has nothing to lose and everything to gain by giving these tactics a fair trial. In any eventuality, she needs to know that she is equal to the problem posed by a neurotic husband. She should be able to deal with it on an intellectual level, rather than with wrathful tears or running away.

There is another type of neurotic husband who, instead of withdrawing, comes looking for a fight. He is irritable, abusive, sarcastic. He provokes argument at every turn. Unconsciously, he wants to keep things in turmoil; he wants others to be as miserable and upset as he is. He can forget his own inner unrest in a rousing fight—and thereby escape from what's really bothering him. It is a blundering and bad kind of therapy he has discovered for himself, destructive of his own happiness and that of all those around him.

His is the shouting temper. Never irritate it. Never raise your voice to a neurotic husband. Do not be his mirror. Like our no-argument rule, this one too is primary in dealing with the difficult husband.

Let such a husband talk—or shout himself out—without making the mistake of trying to justify yourself or forcing him to hear your point of view. Bide your time. Say no more than, "You're upset over this now—let's talk about it some other time."

The cooling-off period will do more to bring him around to being reasonable than all the quarreling in the world.

When a psychiatrist's patient becomes abusive, the psychiatrist makes no answer, offers no defense. The patient is brought up short, like a man running headlong at a locked door only to find it opens at a touch. His anger dies for lack of opposition.

If you keep your patience every time a neurotic husband explodes, he will gradually drop this particular line of attack for want of response. There's no satisfaction in beating on a blank wall. Your silence, too, gives him a chance to hear himself shout, and he realizes that he is going to extremes.

To shout back at one you know to be nervously upset is, in a way, false pride. You feel you have to defend your position, argue your side of the issue. You usually ask yourself later, "Why do I do it? It's useless." You are right.

There is a definite reason why we cannot tolerate at close range anyone with neurotic traits. It's our fear of identification. We begin to wonder if the affliction is contagious, as we find ourselves responding to a neurotic person in a similarly unbalanced way. He shouts at us; we shout back—it becomes a vicious circle.

Everyone likes to be around normal people—their energy, their good spirits are contagious. So if we resist the moods of the neurotically beset, we may make them the imitators of our normal behavior.

Sometimes pressures of one kind or another put a neurotic husband on the borderline of violence. It may take just a few angry words to send him over. Never challenge a neurotic husband to violence. The wife, tired of her husband's jealousy, his envy of more successful men or his pessimism, may say, "All right—there's the window. Go ahead and jump." And he will.

Suicide threats will usually cease when there is no satisfying reaction to them. Remember that we are all under the strain of life's hardships, and we can use either destructive or constructive means to meet that strain. We should be taught that the choice of means is ours.

Women find themselves in the position of having to make a choice as to what they will do about the neurotic husband in need of strength. Let him sink—or help him swim? The chances are that, except in the most drastic cases, to detach yourself from the neurotic husband's life and let him go unaided will leave you with a feeling of having failed to meet a problem.

You yourself will benefit in the long run by educating yourself to deal intelligently and patiently not only with the *problem husband* but with all the neurotic and distraught people you encounter. And there is literally no situation involving a neurotic personality that will not be alleviated by these simple rules:

1. Keep your voice quiet.
2. Allow a generous cooling-off period.
3. Give every situation the benefit of a delayed and thought-out response.

Consider the old parable of the contest between the wind and the sun, each trying to make the traveler remove his coat. The wind *shouted* and howled with all its might, but the traveler clung tighter to his coat. Then the sun warmed him, and gradually the traveler loosed his hold on the coat, then relinquished it altogether.

The neurotic husband will relinquish his desperate hold on his cover-up tactics only when he feels he no longer needs their protection—when he receives assurance that the storm is over and that the sun of human affection is, in his case, out to stay.

Remind yourself that your *frigidity* may represent a *symptom-reaction* to your husband's *neurotic* personality.

Therefore, it would be wise to establish a more harmonious personality relationship between yourself and your husband, through the application of some of the suggestions described above, if you wish to achieve *greater sexual satisfaction.*

3.

THE MALE AND FEMALE SEXUAL APPARATUS

The Male Sexual Organs and Their Function

A knowledge of the anatomy and physiology of the sexual organs of both sexes is of practical importance in the sex education of the average woman.

For example, the woman who understands the mechanism involved in the erection of the penis will appreciate the importance of stimulating her husband mentally and physically. He requires this stimulation in order to sustain his erection and carry out the sexual act.

A patient who had been referred to me because of his failure to maintain an erection stated that his wife had never fondled his penis and insisted that she found it repulsive to consider doing so. When I gave his wife a lecture course in sexual anatomy, she assumed a healthier attitude toward sex in general and toward this problem in particular.

If a woman has an understanding of the role her breasts play—that they are part of her sexual apparatus, that it is normal to have them fondled by her husband during preliminary lovemaking—that stimulating the clitoris brings about the sexual wetness in the vagina necessary for the penetration of the penis—she will have an advantage over the woman who is totally ignorant regarding the anatomy and function of the sexual organs.

A woman who has been educated in sexual matters is more poised during sexual relations, is better able to appreciate what is required for the harmonious completion of the sex act, and is less inclined to become frigid.

The male sexual system consists of the penis, the scrotum, the testicles (equivalent to the ovaries in the woman), the seminal ducts, seminal vesicles and the prostate gland.

The *penis* which is sometimes called the "phallus" (a Greek term) is an appendage that is pendulous and flaccid in its normal state and is referred to as the organ of copulation. It has a canal running through its shaft known as the *urethra* which starts at the bladder and ends at the tip of the penis. The visible aperture of this canal is called the *urethral opening or orifice*. The urethra serves two functions, 1) the discharge of urine from the bladder, and 2) the expulsion of semen from the seminal vesicles.

THE MALE AND FEMALE SEXUAL APPARATUS

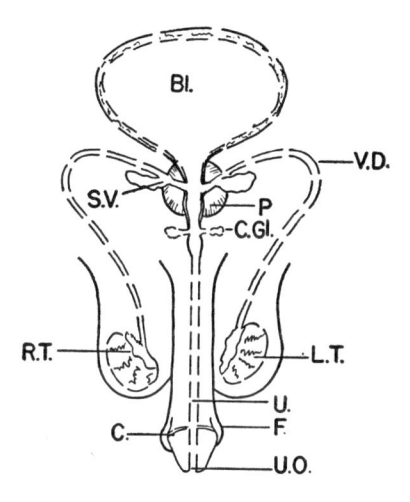

Bl.—Bladder
C.—Corona
C.Gl.—Cowper's Gland
F.—Foreskin
L.T.—Left Testicle
P.—Prostate Gland
R.T.— Right Testicle
S.—Scrotum
S.V.—Seminal Vesicle
U.—Urethra
U.O.—Urethral Orifice
V.D.—Vas Deferens

The Male Sexual System

During an erection caused by sexual excitement, the penis becomes rigid and enlarged. The urethra may exude a sticky mucouslike secretion (urethral saliva, the product of what are called Cowper's Glands) which lubricates the urethral canal prior to ejaculation of semen. The erection is caused by the flow of blood through the many blood vessels of the corpora cavernosa (the spongy vascular substance of the penis) which causes the penis to swell under the influence of sexual excitement. This rigidity and expansion of the penis is a prerequisite for coitus. It involves the nervous system. The desire for sexual relief comes from erotic stimuli in the brain transmitted to the penis via certain nerve routes along the spinal canal. This mechanism may be likened to an electric current passing through wires connected to a battery. Stimulating thoughts that influence the erection center in the brain will result in messages sent to the penis by way of the nervous system causing the penis to expand. Any disturbing thoughts or conflicts, however, associated with sexual frustrations may result in an opposite reaction resulting in a failure of the penis to become erect. This occurs among men who are extremely sensitive, inexperienced and susceptible to frustrations.

Sometimes an erection occurs not only from thoughts

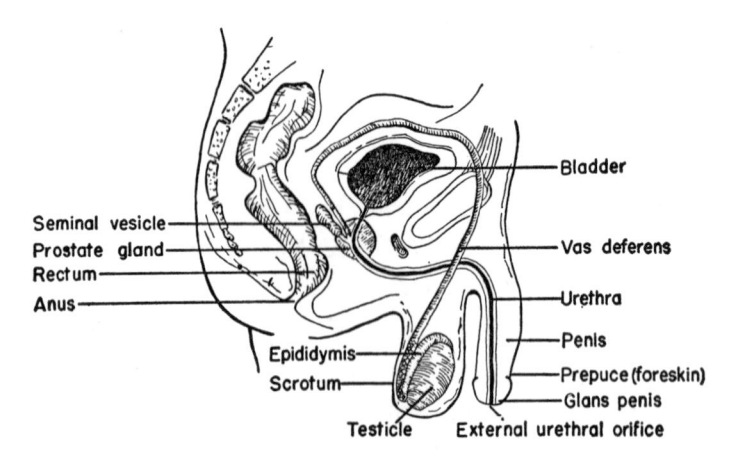

The Male Sexual Apparatus
(Cross Section)

which excite the imagination but automatically from a full bladder, stimulating substances called "aphrodisiacs" (named after the Greek goddess of love, Aphrodite), and irritations from tight clothing or accumulated secretions around the head of the penis. The so-called morning erection is generally caused by the urge to urinate.

An erection can also be brought about, of course, by rubbing the penis against something or the manual mechanical to and fro movements of the *foreskin* or *prepuce* surrounding the penis (masturbation).

In boys and some men the covering of the head of the penis by the foreskin is called "phimosis" which can be removed by circumcision.

The head of the penis is spoken of as the *glans*—and is very sensitive particularly around its base or *corona*. It becomes the focal seat of pleasurable sensations and in the uncircumcized man is kept moistened by a sebaceous secretion known as *smegma* necessitating the frequent washing of the penis in order to eliminate unpleasant sexual odors or irritation from its accumulation.

The *scrotum* is a muscular tissue sac beneath the penis containing the two testicles.

The *testicles* are two oval-shaped bodies which are suspended in the scrotum and are about the size of plums. Usually the left testicle hangs lower than the right. This sometimes creates concern among men who believe they should hang symmetrically.

A cross-section of a testicle exhibits numerous *seminiferi-*

ous tubules filled with sperm cells. These sperm cells or *spermatazoa* are shaped like a tadpole and consist of a head, neck and tail. They are contained in the *semen* which are expelled or ejaculated from the penis coincidental with sexual climax. The tubules of each testicle converge toward a common meeting place known as the epididymis which in turn leads to the *seminal duct* or *Vas Deferens*—the tube that carries the sperm cells from the testicle to the *seminal vesicle* (a reservoir for accumulated spermatazoa) located behind the prostate. A surgical operation involving the ligation or cutting (vasectomy) of this tube produces artificial sterilization in the male. Such an operation incidentally does not eliminate sexual desire.

From the seminal vesicles the semen passes through two ejaculatory ducts into the prostatic portion of the urethra.

An ejaculation is caused by the spasmodic contractions of the muscle fibers of the penis. The semen that is expelled is made up of spermatazoa, the secretion of the prostate gland, seminal vesicles and urethra. It is grayish-white, sticky and has a characteristic odor. One ejaculation yields approximately a teaspoonful of semen containing millions of sperm cells. These spermatazoa are motile and under a microscope can be seen swimming about in different directions.

The automatic emptying of the seminal vesicles during sleep is spoken of as a *nocturnal emission* (or "wet dream"), which is a normal phenomenon.

THE MALE AND FEMALE SEXUAL APPARATUS 67

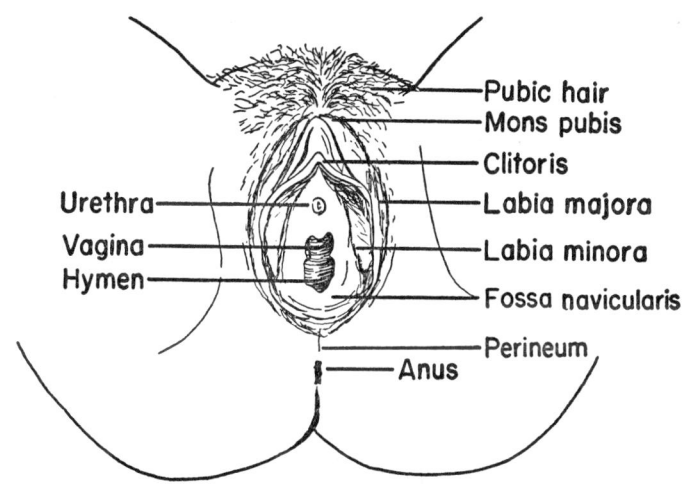

The Female Sexual System
(External Genitalia)

The Female Sexual Organs

The female sexual system consists of external and internal organs. The external genitalia include the vulva, labia majora, labia minora, vestibule, urethral opening, vaginal entrance, and the clitoris.

The *vulva* is merely an all-inclusive term referring to the external genitalia of a woman. At the anterior end of the vulva is located a mound or protuberance known as the *Mons Pubis,* also called the *Mons Veneris,* covered with pubic hair arranged in the form of a triangle. The vulva itself consists of two outer lips (*labia majora*) and two inner lips (the *labia minora*). The latter converge at the upper portion of the vulva to form the *clitoris*—a protruding nipple of flesh which is the seat of pleasurable sensations.

The two outer lips or labia majora are also covered with pubic hair and serve to cover the opening of the vagina.

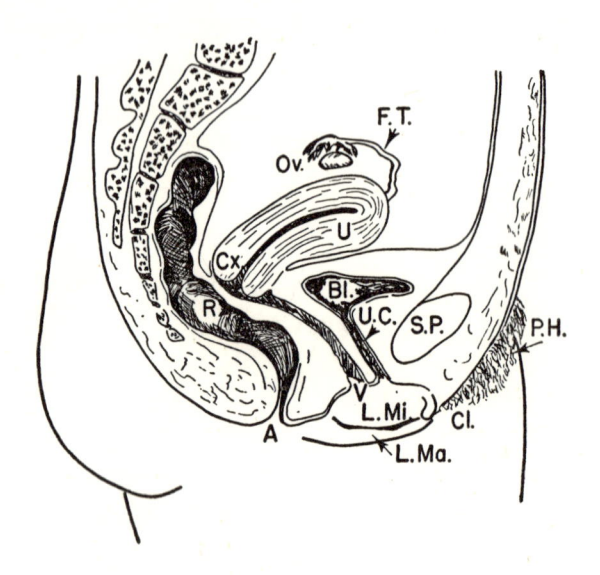

A – Anus
Bl.—Bladder
Cl.—Clitoris
Cx.—Cervix
F.T.—Fallopian Tube
L.Ma.—Labia Majora
L.Mi.— Labia Minora

Ov.— Ovary
P.H.—Pubic Hair
R—Rectum
S.P.—Symphysis Pubis
U—Uterus
U.C.—Urethral Canal
V–Vagina

The Female Sexual System
(Cross Section)

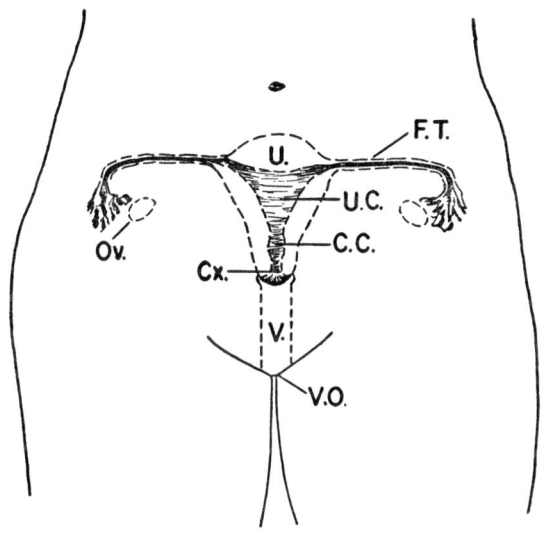

C.C.—Cervical Canal
Cx.—Cervix
F.T.—Fallopian Tube
Ov.—Ovary
U.C.—Uterine Cavity
U.—Uterus (womb)
V.—Vagina
V.O.—Vaginal Orifice

The Female Reproductive Organs

Within these two folds of flesh can be found two smaller reddish-colored ones, sometimes referred to as *nymphae*. Between them can be seen a small aperture known as the *urethral orifice*. It leads to a small canal, the *urethra*, connected with the bladder and serves as a passageway for urination. Below this urethra is found the *vaginal entrance* which receives the penis and is surrounded by muscle fibers which are capable of contraction when the penis is introduced, adding to the pleasure of the male. Many women learn to contract the muscles of their vagina voluntarily during coitus in order to enhance their pleasurable feelings.

Just within the opening leading to the vagina is located the *hymen*—a thin, perforated, circular, elastic membrane found in virgins. The act of tearing the hymen by introducing the penis for the first time is spoken of as *defloration*.

Some women rupture their hymen by horseback riding, riding a bicycle, or by introducing various objects into their vagina for masturbatory purposes.

The space between the vaginal entrance and the urethra is called the *vestibule* while the area behind the vaginal opening is spoken of as the *perineum* (a space between the vagina and the anus, the latter referring to the outer opening into the rectum).

The internal female apparatus consists of two ovaries, two narrow hollow tubes, the uterus or womb and the vagina.

The *ovaries* are two glands about the size of large olives, located on the right and left side of the uterus and serve to produce ova or eggs.

The tubes (*Fallopian tubes*) are connected to the ovaries by a structure that resembles a funnel called the *infundibulum* and serve to transport the eggs to the uterus. Hence they are sometimes called the *oviducts*. When the fertilized egg meets the sperm of the male in the cavity of the womb and union takes place (*conception*) it is embedded in the wall of the uterus and develops into a child. It becomes an *embryo* at first and later becomes a *foetus* (the technical name for the unborn child) which is surrounded by a bag of water (the *amniotic fluid*). The foetus receives its nutrition from the maternal blood supply by means of the *placenta* (afterbirth) and the *umbilical cord* (an umbrella-like arrangement).

The womb or uterus is a muscular, elastic hollow organ in size and shape like an inverted pear. It is suspended by ligaments in the lower abdomen or pelvis of the woman and is tipped slightly forward to allow for expansion during pregnancy. The neck or mouth of the womb is known as the *cervix* and connects with the internal end of the vagina. In time of pregnancy the uterus expands which accounts for the protuberance of the abdominal walls until the mother delivers her child. Labor pains are caused by the contractions of the muscular walls of the uterus in an attempt to expel the newborn child.

The *vagina* is an internal passageway that receives the penis and leads to the cervix. It is also muscular and capable of grasping the introduced penis in a pleasurable manner, and lined by mucous membrane which is lubricated during sexual excitement by a secretion from two mucous glands, known as *Bartholin's Glands,* located at the entrance of the vagina.

Menstruation, or monthly bleeding, which lasts from two to six days is caused by the periodic expulsion, approximately every twenty-eight days, of egg cells contained in bloody fluid (menstrual blood). During pregnancy, menstruation ceases. Many women have menstrual complaints consisting of premenstrual symptoms (fatigue, tension, depression, etc.) and cramps after menstruation has started. Some of these complaints, particularly when they are exaggerated, are influenced by psychological factors. Some neurotic women resent the need for having to menstruate and the accompanying discomfort. Many women refer to this phenomenon as the "curse."

Menopause, or the climacteric, refers to those years in a woman's life around the forty-fifth year when menstruation ceases altogether, and is very often associated with symptoms of psychological origin.

Because of its transitional nature, it is commonly spoken of as a woman's "change of life" during which time many women experience personality changes.

The word "clitoris" is derived from the Greek meaning "key." According to Dr. D. O. Cauldwell, the ancient anatomists may have considered the clitoris as "the key to woman's sexuality"—hence the name.

It is a protuberance of flesh about one-half inch to one inch in length, found at the upper triangle of the vulva, just below the mons pubis. It corresponds to, and resembles, the penis of a man, to the extent that some medical dictionaries refer to it as the "penis Muliebris" (penis of woman). It also has a glans, a foreskin around its tip and is capable of becoming erect. During sexual excitement it becomes extremely sensitive and when manipulated digitally causes the woman to experience voluptuous pleasure.

Men who are aware of the important role of the clitoris in sex technique stimulate this area prior to actual penetration causing the woman to become increasingly excited. Like the penis, the clitoris also becomes engorged with blood which causes it to expand and become rigid. It is kept moistened by a secretion known as smegma and thus requires hygienic care in order to eliminate offensive odors.

The clitoris serves to furnish the woman with increased pleasure during intercourse. Friction against the clitoris as a result of coital movements during intercourse helps a woman achieve her orgasm.

4.

THE ORGASM

It is surprising how many women are frigid simply because they do not know what to expect from intercourse in the way of an orgasm. There are some women who do not even know what the term "orgasm" or what the word "climax" refers to. Occasionally, a patient will say: "Doctor, I don't know whether I have ever experienced an orgasm or not. How does a woman know if she reaches a 'climax?'" Others know quite definitely that they never had a coital orgasm and have no knowledge as to what it takes to achieve an orgasm. There are sexually ignorant husbands who do not know that women are capable of having an orgasm.

THE ORGASM

Nevertheless, the sex education of a woman would be incomplete without some mention of the orgasm.

According to Drs. Willy, Vander and Fisher, authors of the "Encyclopedia Of Sex," not more than one-half of all women experience during the sexual act, voluptuous pleasure rising to the intensity of orgasm."

An orgasm is the result of a sexual impulse produced by physical or mental stimulation conveyed from the brain to the sexual organs, which become engorged with blood causing them to be warmer than other parts of the body. The clitoris becomes erect and swollen. As the sexual excitement increases a lubricating secretion is emitted into the vaginal passageway. This fluid or secretion comes from glands known as Bartholin's glands and constitutes the "sexual wetness" that prepares the vagina for a penetration by the penis. The vagina and clitoris become increasingly sensitive and upon insertion of the penis the muscles of the vagina contract. As the penis begins its to and fro movements the woman begins to experience voluptuous sensations within the vagina. Usually there is some friction made against the clitoris by the approximation of the man's pubic bone against it, which adds to the ecstasy of intercourse. This pleasurable feeling extends within the vagina up to the mouth of the uterus or womb.

The breathing becomes heavy and rapid, the pulse quickens, the excitement increases, the body movements become uncontrollable and the woman may display audible signs of an approaching climax by moaning or verbalizing how wonderful it feels. As the pitch of excitement increases, (the stage known as *tumescence*) she slides into the next stage—that of the actual orgasm or climax referred to as *detumescence*. The word "tumescence" means swelling and "detumescence" refers to unswelling. Hence an orgasm is equivalent to the sudden expulsion of air from an inflated tire. It has sometimes been described as a "floating on clouds" feeling or a "riding the waves." Some claim it is a pleasurable, sinking feeling. Others state that it is a sudden state of oblivion—a momentary departure from consciousness or reality and an excursion into a world of ecstasy. Many husbands are able to time their ejaculation to coincide with their wives' convulsive orgasms.

When a woman experiences an orgasm the intense excitement becomes converted into a final state of pleasant physical and mental relaxation. There is a feeling of *satisfaction* whereby the woman for the time being no longer requires continued sexual stimulation. It is equivalent to the feeling of satisfaction following the ingestion of a well-enjoyed meal. There are some women who are capable of experiencing more than one orgasm within a relatively short period of time. Women respond sexually in accordance with the various factors involved—as for example the extent of their sexual appetite on a particular occasion, the technique of their partner, the environment and other factors that influence the enjoyment of the act.

There are many ways in which a woman can achieve an orgasm and consequently orgasms differ in intensity depending upon the method resorted to in bringing about the ultimate climax.

Women who masturbate, for example, bring about self-induced orgasms by manipulating their clitoris with their finger.

In homosexual practices the clitoris plays a major role in the production of a mutual orgasm. The act of one woman approximating her clitoris to the clitoris of another woman by lying on top of her and simulating coital movements is known as tribadism.

The oral stimulation of the clitoris with the tongue is spoken of as cunnilingus. According to leading investigators, the practice of cunnilingus by men is fairly common. They also report that many women are incapable of experiencing an orgasm during coitus but can achieve one via friction on the clitoris either manually or orally.

Psychoanalysts have found that some women have an exaggerated sensitivity of the clitoris (a fixation of their sexual instinct to this particular organ instead of the vagina). In certain cases the clitoris has been conditioned to a localization of sex pleasure because of excessive masturbation via digital manipulation.

There are a number of unconscious psychological factors involved when women are unable to experience a vaginal orgasm (coital climax), but can get one if the husband stimulates the clitoris with his finger. Such a condition requires psychiatric consultation, Psychoanalysts have found, for instance, that some women unconsciously reject the male organ psychologically speaking, and become frigid during actual intercourse, but will allow themselves to achieve an orgasm by letting the husband masturbate them.

Wilhelm Stekel refers to such women as harboring an unconscious "will to displeasure"—the refusal to enjoy intercourse. Alfred Adler explains it through his "masculine-protest" theory the meaning of which is implied in the term itself. Other psychoanalysts speak of the "renunciation of womanhood" or "denial of the role of the vagina" theory.

At any rate, whenever a woman is incapable of achieving an orgasm via coitus, provided the husband is an adequate partner, and prefers clitoral stimulation to any other form of sexual activity, she can be regarded as suffering from frigidity and requires psychiatric assistance.

There are women who introduce a penis substitute into the vagina (vaginal masturbation), and achieve an orgasm by means of a to and fro motion that can simulate the act of intercourse. These penis substitutes may consist of anything that may resemble the male organ in consistency or shape. Then there are women who can experience an orgasm by merely kissing the lover on the lips in a passionate manner. Many women experience the equivalent of a "wet dream" common to men by dreaming of making love to an imaginary lover.

These *psychic orgasms* in women brought about by mental masturbation are not too uncommon. I have had quite a number of patients who claimed they were unable to achieve sexual satisfaction with their husbands. When I probed into their sex life I discovered that they were experiencing mental masturbation during their sleep. Naturally, a woman who achieves orgasms in her dreams several times a week is less apt to respond to her husband's lovemaking. She apparently finds it more pleasurable to be gratified by her private harem of male lovers in her sleep. While it is true that most women require a longer time for preliminary love play and cannot get an orgasm from intercourse unless the husband delays the ejaculation, there are other women capable of reaching a climax a few minutes after the penis is inserted. This would tend to prove that the ability of a woman to attain an orgasm is dependent upon her attitude toward intercourse, her power of concentration, her willingness to cooperate, the extent of her wanting to enjoy sex relations and her ability to abandon herself completely to the pleasurable sensation of the sex act.

A man is quick to be aroused, as compared to a woman, and is more apt to achieve his orgasm in a much shorter time. The duration of the orgasm is also less. In a woman, on the contrary, the orgasm is generally prolonged. She continues to experience pleasurable sensations within her vagina, even though she has reached a climax. Her orgasm is influenced by the technique of her husband and his behavior toward her during the lovemaking.

Some women claim they experience one intensive orgasm at the peak of the sexual act, while others experience a series of orgasms from the time the penis is inserted until it is withdrawn. This type of chain-reactions or multiple orgasms does not occur among men.

One patient surprisingly enough claimed she was able to achieve an orgasm from anilingus and described the orgasm as being very erotic but quite different than the orgasm she experienced from coitus. She experiences a quivering of the "sphincter ani" muscles and muscles of the vagina at the time of the orgasm.

Another patient admitted she was able to reach a climax during the husband's sucking of her nipples.

It is possible, therefore, for some women to bring about an orgasm by excitement or stimulation of almost any kind. I once encountered a patient who reluctantly admitted she was able to enjoy a sexual thrill at the race track watching the horses come down the home stretch.

Many women achieve the equivalent of a mild orgasm from a love scene at the movies or from reading literature considered salacious.

Sometimes a change in position will aid some women in achieving an orgasm.

In the psychiatric treatment of sexually inadequate women it is important to investigate these so-called *orgasm-detours*.

It is the *orgasm* that is primarily beneficial to the health of the individual. Sexual stimulation without sexual relief via the orgasm is responsible, as previously stated, for many nervous disorders among frigid women.

In discussing the subject of frigidity with leading gynecologists, I learned that many of their patients come to them complaining of a host of psychosomatic ailments, and are reluctant to discuss their intimate sex life, thinking it has no bearing on their symptoms. Once the doctor establishes the necessary rapport with his patient she confides in him and begins to relate the details of her sexual dissatisfactions. The frigid woman is more likely to go to a gynecologist first, and when he finds that there is no physical basis for her complaints, and suspects that they are caused by a sexual frustration, he refers her to a psychiatrist. Many of these referred patients harbor a number of fallacies regarding the orgasm. Some believe, for instance, that they can never have a child because they have never achieved a sexual climax during intercourse. Others believe that their frigidity is congenital, and that they are hopelessly incapable of experiencing sex pleasure. While still others feel that the sexual act is consummated for procreation purposes only and to abandon themselves to the ecstasy of the sex act is sinful.

Several gynecologists have told me that patients who underwent hysterectomies (the surgical removal of the ovaries, tubes and womb) often became depressed because they felt they would no longer be able to achieve orgasms. I have had a number of patients of my own who complained of having become frigid following a hysterectomy, only because they harbored the *misconception* that their capacity for sex enjoyment disappears with the removal of their internal reproductive organs. In many instances the woman who has had a hysterectomy is able to achieve a vaginal orgasm during intercourse with greater ease now that she is no longer handicapped by her previous fear of becoming pregnant.

The gynecologist who treats his cases of frigidity with injections of various hormones over a prolonged period of time, ignoring the psychological factors involved, will have on his hands patients who became more neurotic as a result of their unhappiness and disappointment.

The vast amount of current literature in psychosomatic medicine has convinced the majority of gynecologists that frigidity for the most part is psychological in origin. Proof of this lies in the fact that psychoanalysts have been definitely able to cure women of their frigidity via psychotherapy. By a process of reeducation a woman can learn how to overcome the inhibitions that very often prevent her from achieving a sexual orgasm.

5.

TYPES OF FRIGIDITY

General Considerations

Frigidity is a symptom-disturbance in the psychosexual development of women, causing them to find it difficult to achieve a vaginal orgasm during sexual intercourse. It is the commonest of sexual disorders among women. As previously explained, it does not always refer to sexual coldness or indifference on the part of a woman to sex relations.

Some women are less passionate than others but this is due to conditioning rather than heredity. Women are capable of experiencing as much sex desire as found among men. In fact many women can enjoy several orgasms in the course of a single sexual act. This would tend to support the theory that frigid women are *blocked* from enjoying sex because of their inhibitions, repressions and inability to give vent to the full expression of their sexual cravings. Frigidity, therefore, can be construed as a form of "self-denial."

There are women who achieve a vaginal orgasm occasionally. Others never seem to experience a "climax" during coitus. Still others claim they find intercourse pleasurable, but are unable to reach a climax.

Frigidity may be an unconscious way of punishing a man. Stekel makes the assertion that "almost every woman is capable of arresting the orgasm; some women actually exercise their will-to-displeasure in order not to succumb to their husbands."

Take by way of illustration a man who becomes abusive and undeserving of his wife's affection. As a husband he demands physical gratification. He performs his carnal pleasure-act but becomes mentally dissatisfied because she displays no "readiness for love." It can be said that at the very crisis of the sexual act, the wife hears an inner voice say, "Now is your opportunity to display your sexual authority; punish him, take the pleasure out of his affection."

There are thousands of these anesthetic daughters of Venus or as the French call them "femmes de glace" (Women of Ice).

One investigator claims that forty percent of all married women derive little or no pleasure from the sexual act. Many of these wives pretend they are experiencing an orgasm in order to deceive their husbands. They dislike admitting that they are frigid.

A frigid wife is capable of causing impotence in the male. The husband becomes frustrated at the thought that his wife is not sexually satisfied after intercourse. Knowing that she is incapable of sharing the pleasure of sex relations he becomes less interested in approaching his wife.

There are many types of frigidity. The causes of frigidity depend upon the type involved.

The Different Kinds of Frigidity

Many investigators have attempted to classify various types of frigidity according to causative factors or types of reactions to stimulation and other criteria.

The following represents some of the different kinds of frigidity which psychiatrists encounter in their practice.

1. *Honeymoon frigidity.* It is found among virgins who are unable to achieve a vaginal orgasm during intercourse because of the pain involved in the rupture of their hymen by the male organ. The sexual initiation is remembered as an unpleasant experience. The incidence of honeymoon frigidity is apparently on the decline as evidenced by the estimates of Dr. Lewis Terman, Dr. John McPartland and others, that, "some seventy percent of women today are fully rehearsed in what to expect on their honeymoon."

2. *Frigidity caused by organic lesions of the pelvic organs.* These conditions need to be investigated by gynecologists. It is difficult for a woman to experience an orgasm when she finds the sex act painful because of some inflammation of her external or internal sexual organs.

3. *Frigidity caused by the husband's sexual inadequacy.* These women are unable to attain an orgasm because their husbands suffer from some form of impotence, such as premature ejaculation or an inability to sustain an erection or faulty technique. These women are often capable of experiencing an orgasm with men other than their husbands. Hence their orgasm incapacity in a marriage to a sexually inadequate husband is sometimes referred to as *relative frigidity*. When the husband's sexual disorder is corrected by the psychiatrist and his technique is improved, the wife begins to experience coital orgasms.

4. *Frigidity caused by a fear of pregnancy.* This is a rather common type of frigidity. Women who are burdened with more children than they are able to raise often develop an aversion to sex, and are unable to respond because of being preoccupied with the responsibilities of another pregnancy. They are unable to relax during intercourse. Such women respond when the fear of pregnancy is eliminated.

5. *Frigidity caused by psychic trauma.* Many wives who complain of frigidity give a history of some unpleasant sexual experience in early life. They were either accosted sexually in early childhood by a member of the family or a

relative or became pregnant during adolescence and are trying to forget the unpleasantness of an abortion, which they fear may come to light someday. Or they have been subjected to some other kind of damaging experience leaving a lasting impression on their sex life.

6. *Frigidity caused by inhibition, prudishness, false modesty, fears of various kinds, and sex ignorance.* This has sometimes been referred to as pseudo frigidity. With proper reeducation of attitudes toward sex and adequate insight into the complexes impeding their response, these women can soon develop the capacity to enjoy sex relations.

7. *Frigidity caused by guilt.* In this group are classified the many women who, because of harboring some past or present guilt in connection with sex, are unable to abandon themselves to the pleasures of the sex act. Women who are promiscuous often suffer from orgasm-incapacity because of unconscious guilt resulting from their dissipations.

8. *Frigidity associated with narcissism (self-love).* This type is common to women who are beautiful and who are unable to concentrate on the sex act because of being preoccupied with their own love of themselves.

9. *Frigidity associated with masculine-protest reactions.* These women harbor an antimale psychology. They are masculine in behavior, overaggressive, dominating, cynical, sarcastic, overcritical and have an inability to establish a normal, healthy love relationship with the opposite sex. Lesbians, both the overt and latent types, come under this

category. A wife who harbors strong feelings of hostility toward her husband would naturally find it more difficult to achieve orgasms than one who loves her husband.

10. Frigidity caused by circumstantial frustrations. A wife may complain of not having attained an orgasm during intercourse because of a distraction, interruption, or is handicapped by a fear of being seen or heard having sex relations. A knock on the door, or a child walking into the bedroom may cause a woman to become sufficiently frustrated as to interfere with her resuming sex relations.

Frigidity can also be classified according to the nature of the response or rather degree of frigidity. For example, there are women who claim they are unable to achieve an orgasm of any kind, no matter what method is used to stimulate them. They have what psychiatrists refer to as an *anesthesia of the vagina*—an absence of any pleasurable feelings in the vagina during intercourse. Such a woman may show no interest in sex and may even express a desire to have intercourse over with as quickly as possible. In some instances she may even state that she finds sex repulsive and disgusting. The vagina is usually dry and she may develop a tenseness of the muscles of the vagina (vaginismus) as an unconscious expression of rejection of the male organ. Then there is a type of frigidity in contrast to the type just described, in which the woman finds the sex act pleasurable but cannot reach a climax.

There is a large group who may be classified as the *clitoral type,* insofar as they can experience an orgasm only if the clitoris is manipulated digitally or orally. But they do not have a sexual climax from intercourse alone.

It is not too uncommon to encounter women who are frigid and who classify as the *nymphomanic type*. These women find sexual relations extremely pleasurable and show evidence of being very passionate and responsive, but they never seem to achieve a vaginal orgasm during coitus. They may or may not achieve an orgasm from other methods of gratification, such as masturbation of the clitoris.

Nymphomania actually denotes an excessive craving for sexual relations in women whose sexual appetite is never adequately gratified. It is a craving for sex for its own sake.

A woman who suffers from nymphomania is said to have a "Messalina Complex." The latter term is derived from the name of a notorious female (Messalina) who lived during the days of the Roman Empire. She is alleged to have given herself to numerous men because of her insatiable appetite for sexual intercourse.

I once treated a young woman who had been previously married and divorced and who craved sex relations with any man who became her escort for the evening. She worried about what she called a "weakness" and wanted to learn how to develop sufficient will power to become discreet. She had gotten into difficulties with married men on numerous occasions.

Her early history disclosed excessive masturbation through manual manipulation of the clitoris. She admitted an inability to achieve an orgasm during sexual intercourse.

She experienced no pleasurable sensations in the vagina (anesthesia vaginalis). Her promiscuity and nymphomania represented an attempt in fantasy to meet some man who would enable her to experience an orgasm during sexual intercourse.

Hitschman and Bergler cite the case of a frigid woman who changed lovers frequently because she believed they and not she were responsible for her frigidity. She would repeat to each lover after intercourse "You are just as incapable of satisfying me as all the others." This was her way of achieving revenge satisfaction.

Incidentally, many frigid wives, because of being deprived of sexual satisfaction, get vicarious revenge by spending their husband's money quite freely—or going to many doctors and specialists incurring large medical bills, or ultimately divorcing them in order to get a substantial alimony settlement (what victim-husbands refer to as "blood money").

There is also a type of frigidity common to women who are able to become sexually aroused by preliminary lovemaking, and who experience a sexual wetness following stimulation but who cool off quickly once intercourse has begun. This type is equivalent to a type of impotence in the male characterized by a man having a good erection but loses it as soon as he begins to insert his penis into the vagina.

Psychologically and emotionally these women are virgin-wives. They carry over into the marriage relationship the attitude they had during their pre-marital experiences when they indulged in kissing and petting, but refused to engage in intercourse. They fail to understand that this approach to sex must be abandoned once they enter the marital state.

The proper classification of frigidity is of course essential to the adequate treatment of this condition. Some cases are easier to treat than others, as will be shown in a later section of this chapter.

Personality Deviations Associated with Frigidity

Since frigidity is considered a symptom manifestation of some underlying neurosis, it is more apt to develop in women who are nervous, tense, unrelaxed and who possess a so-called neurotic personality. Many of them are unable to *concentrate* on the sexual relationship with their husbands.

The following represent the types of personality deviations that are most apt to result in the development of frigidity among various types of neurotic women. Their emotional immaturity, moodiness, fears, anxieties and complexes all tend to interfere with their sexual responses. They are unable to concentrate on the sex act, exercise poor judgment in what they say during lovemaking and may have an inability to love anyone other than themselves.

1. The Anti-Male (Masculine-Protest) type. The term

"masculine-protest" was first used by the famous psychologist, Alfred Adler, to describe a large group of women who subconsciously derive satisfaction from protesting against everything a man says or does.

A marriage with a woman of this kind becomes a competitive struggle for supremacy. We say she is "ambivalent," to borrow a term from the vocabulary of the psychoanalysts, capable of loving and hating her husband, depending upon her whims. Overaggressiveness is her outstanding fault. Aggressiveness in a wife can be an asset, but too much of it leads to incompatibility, like having too much pepper in your food.

This type of woman is obsessed with an urge to dominate the male sex. She is innately argumentative. Whether or not she pursues a career, her husband occupies a secondary role in her life.

A husband once told me, "My wife can't be bothered with a home and having children. She claims it would interfere with her career. She likes to travel, to see new faces and refuses to think of her marital obligations."

Another patient, an attractive unmarried woman of 22, stated emphatically, "When I marry I am going to insist on having the right to go out with my former men friends. I can't see why marriage should make things different. I want to enjoy complete independence." She wanted marriage without a partnership.

The Masculine-Protest wife fulfills her sexual obligations from a sense of duty rather than a desired gratification.

Frigidity, therefore, is common to this type of woman. It represents an expression of their refusal to be loved by any man. They refuse to assume a receptive role. Their self-hatred is projected in the form of hatred of the opposite sex. In short, they do not enjoy the role of being a woman. They do not wish to give a man the satisfaction that he is capable of making them enjoy the sex act. Psychologically and emotionally, these women are still virgin wives. They generally are overattached to an "ideal" father or brother (no man can ever measure up to the wonderful qualities of their fathers or brothers, so that they look upon their husband as an inferior specimen of a man). Or they are daughters of an indifferent father (an alcoholic, gambler or philanderer) and are unable to develop a normal love relationship to a husband because all men, including the husband, represent the undesirable father substitute. This reaction is entirely subconscious.

In this group we find women who commit adultery in revenge when they discover their husbands have been flirting or unfaithful.

To this masculine-protest group often belong women who have an aversion to marriage and family life. As to housework, this wife either assumes a who-cares attitude, or she is fanatically meticulous. You know the latter kind—the husband is constantly nagged to empty the ash tray, pick up the newspaper or magazine from the floor, or hang up his coat. Such a wife is tactless, temperamental and unable to differentiate between nagging and making suggestions. She is stubborn, sensitive and intolerant. She spends the bulk of her time trying to remake her husband in the presence of friends. Those who know her remark: "You can tell who wears the pants in that family."

Masculine-protest wives usually leave the altar with a ring on the finger and a chip on the shoulder. Their children often become targets for feelings of hostility really directed against the husband.

Nature intended a woman to be feminine, affectionate and passive. She can be helpfully persuasive. But when her aggressiveness far exceeds this, she becomes a "personality freak." She becomes her own enemy and prevents her husband from ever making a good adjustment to marriage.

The neurotic woman recognizing in herself this "will to dominate" and endeavoring to overcome it has already taken the first major step toward becoming a better woman.

2. *The Emotionally Unstable (Hysterical) Type.* The term "hysterical" comes from the Greek word meaning "womb." It was believed that a woman's moods fluctuated because of periodic changes in her uterus or womb. Hence, the expression "hysterical" came into use to describe women who are emotionally unstable. This type is also prone to develop sexual frigidity.

The "hysteric" is endowed with a health-complaining (hypochondriacal) disposition. She goes from one doctor to another seeking a cure for her many ailments. Her mental conflicts have become converted into physical symptoms but no one can convince her that there is nothing wrong with her health. She derives both an advantage and outlet in neurotically complaining about her health, a form of malingering. Subconsciously, she may be punishing her husband for one reason or another. Or she may be seeking the kind of sympathy which she got as a child from her parents. In any event, she concocts endless excuses to refrain from having sexual relations with her husband, pleading illness of one form or another.

I recall the case of a patient who had been going to doctors for years, exhausting her husband's income. We discovered that through her neurotic illness she was getting some sort of revenge satisfaction. Her husband admitted he was unable to control his frequent outbursts of anger. The wife reacted to his shouting and anger by running up the doctor's bill.

Women in this group are subject to various kinds of ailments. They may suffer from morbid fears, nervous indigestion, panic states, headaches, weakness, dizziness and a host of other symptoms. They laugh loudly, cry easily and faint at will. They are the "can't take it" type.

The hysterical woman exercises no control over her emotions. She is an actress in constant pursuit of an audience. Without doubt she was a neurotic as a child, and unfortunately her parents catered to her wants and her whims.

This type of woman requires more self-discipline than the masculine-protest woman. She is unable to understand enough about her subconscious self to change knowingly for the better. Since she does not respond to her husband's exhortations, she needs the kind of psychiatrist who will not withhold the truth. What he tells her might be regarded as "shock-therapy," a drug substitute for her hysterical ills.

3. *The Attention-Getting (Narcissistic) type.* Narcissus was a Greek god who fell in love with his own image reflected in a pool of water. A narcissistic woman is one who is in love with herself. If she is beautiful she spends her time looking into mirrors. She becomes a beauty parlor addict and is overconcerned about her hair, nails, face, figure and clothes. If she is not naturally glamorous, she may overcompensate by devoting most of her time to her appearance.

Narcissistic women strive to be the center of attention. They enjoy popularity, are easily flattered and inclined to be flirtatious. They are annoyed if their husbands manifest a jealousy streak. But when a husband exhibits an interest in another woman at a party, he never hears the end of it.

The narcissistic woman is sophisticated, sadistic and delights in teasing the male sex. She delights in exciting men sexually, but derives no pleasure herself from sexual intercourse. A husband of one of my patients declared that he would never again marry a beautiful woman. His ex-wife had been a professional model. He described her utter lack of response to physical affection. All through her childhood she was told how beautiful she was with the result that she never got over her vanity.

In a desire to be overloved the narcissistic woman is unable to give up her self-love. Instead of inspiring her husband to greater achievements, she evaluates the marriage in terms of: "I might have done better considering my ability to attract men." It takes a very tolerant husband to live with this type of spoiled, egotistic wife.

4. The Family-Slave (Adult-Infantilistic) Type. This type is a "child wife," her personality predominantly characterized by emotional immaturity which seriously interferes with her enjoyment of the sex act. A wife belonging to this group runs home to "mama" when the husband becomes thoughtless or a bit abusive or even when he complains about her lack of response in the sexual relationship.

Psychoanalysts refer to these wives as family slaves, insofar as they have never been able to detach themselves emotionally from their relatives. They have a parent fixation and are constantly consulting them, with the result that the husband becomes an aspirin addict because of mother-in-law headaches.

This type is overpossessive, a clinging vine. She cries at the least hurt to her feelings. Emotionally irresponsible, she transfers her child-parent dependency to the husband. She is the opposite of the masculine-protest type, unable to make decisions. Because of her domestic incompetency, she continues to be spoiled by a husband who feels sorry for her.

Actually she wants to remain a child. To grow up and develop emotional maturity entails too much effort. She is plagued with mental laziness. This type of woman is also neurotic but in a different way. She is timid and inhibited and has never learned to become emotionally self-sustaining.

When tragedy strikes, she goes all to pieces, has hysterics or a "nervous breakdown."

She makes a poor housekeeper, careless and untidy, and spends money unwisely. The children get on her nerves. This all becomes further complicated by feelings of lonesomeness and self-pity. Only recently a wife who classifies in this group came to the office to confide that she was contemplating suicide. She proceeded to tell me what a fine husband she had, and how unworthy she was of him, in fact, lacked the qualifications of making a good wife for any man. She stated that she never had to want for anything prior to marriage, never had to dry a dish or dust a piece of furniture. She thought everything of her parents and regretted having to leave home when she married. She sobbed as she told me all this (the melancholy weeping-willow type).

Victims of bad parental influences, many of these wives suffer from lack of elementary mental hygiene, poverty of judgment and absence of insight. They go through their married years wearing smoked glasses.

Yet it must be made clear that no greater mistake can be made by the husband than to think that his neurotic wife is completely responsible for her shortcomings. Reprimanding her for her childishness results only in deepening her despair. To repeat, neurotic wives are sicker than women suffering from a physical ailment. It is far easier to treat a known illness such as pneumonia or appendicitis. But it is altogether a different proposition to expect a woman to help herself when she is fighting a hidden enemy. It often takes psychonalysis to bring to the surface the submerged complexes that actuate the behavior of neurotic wives.

The wisdom of marriage for a neurotic wife lies in recognizing her true personality portrait through self-analysis. Once she has arrived at a personality diagnosis, she has a better chance to effect a cure for herself by changing her behavior-attitude toward her husband.

The husband can cooperate in the meantime by neither pampering his neurotic wife nor becoming indifferent or abusive. Since he understands that there are basic underlying reasons for his wife's neuroticism he can adopt the correct approach. He can offer helpful suggestions, keep himself under control by subjugating his intolerance and seek help and advice if the marriage becomes too trying.

6.

CAUSES OF FRIGIDITY

Introduction

There are a multiplicity of factors responsible for frigidity. The causes of frigidity are so complex that it is often difficult to arrive at the true cause unless one delves deeply into the individual's background.

In the following discussion I have set forth the major causes of frigidity. In discussing these causes I have felt it wise to present a number of case histories that have come to my attention in my practice. They are included because it is my belief that they will enable the reader better to understand the nature and causes of frigidity.

It is a well-established psychological fact that unpleasant

or shocking experiences are often pushed so far back into a person's mind that they seem all but forgotten. When this happens the psychiatrist speaks about these experiences as being in a person's *subconscious* memory. But these buried experiences affect our behavior, nevertheless, and in marriage may cause endless complications, maladjustments and unhappiness. Haven't you heard someone say about themselves, "I don't know why I do it, but I seem to do it all the time." Perhaps you have even thought it about yourself. The fact that you don't understand what motivates you to behave in a certain way doesn't mean that there are no explanations for your behavior. The explanations are there, but the chances are they are buried in your subconscious. We don't remember certain experiences because life would be unbearable if we recalled vividly each painful episode and relived it over and over again.

Yet it is these very subconscious factors, which disturb our lives, that often explain the cause of our unhappiness and failure. We cannot solve these problems by substituting a world of fantasy for reality. Basically, we must come to know ourselves, for in that knowledge lies our strength.

Some of the cases which accompany the discussion of the causes of frigidity may seem unusual. The fact of the matter is that almost all of us have had some experience which, when put on paper, might seem extreme or shocking. The Kinsey Report, among others, has proven to us how large a percentage of the population engage in practices or have had experiences which society may frown upon.

But these are the facts of life. If we are serious about coming to grips with the problems of marriage, divorce, abortion, maladjusted children, etc., we must face these facts of life squarely and not pretend they do not exist. These cases may give the readers some insight into their own problems. It may make it possible for them to face up to what makes them as they are when they realize that others have had similar disturbing experiences. Any such insight or realization is the first step toward a better marriage, a happier home, and a more stable society.

Physical Causes

Frigidity may be due to a variety of physical causes. One may find deficiencies of the internal glands, anemias, vaginitis, menstrual disorders or pelvic anomalies, etc.

Vaginismus (spasm of the muscles of the vagina making insertion of the penis difficult or impossible) can easily be aggravated by psychological factors. Psychoanalysts have found that it often represents a rejection of the penis—an unconscious tendency to *castrate* the male partner.

Vaginismus is a curable condition. A physician once referred a patient to me who suffered from chronic insomnia of three years' duration. She claimed that she had not been able to sleep well since the bridal night. While she made an attempt to submit to the initial coital act on her honeymoon, her husband had never succeeded in inserting his penis in the vagina. A week following the honeymoon she consulted a gynecologist who incised the hymen surgically and dilated the vagina. However, when her husband attempted intercourse, the vagina would contract each time and she complained of severe pain. She returned to the gynecologist who subjected her to an operation consisting of making the vaginal passageway larger. But she still had difficulty. It was presumed that her vaginismus was the result of her fear of coitus. This was revealed in the course of her psychiatric interviews. She had been brought up by puritanical parents to regard sex as something sordid. Unconsciously, she preferred her marriage to be sexless stating that she wanted the *companionship* of her husband but could not accept his physical lovemaking whole-heartedly. It required extensive analysis to overcome her fear of sexual intercourse.

Sex Ignorance and Prudishness

Prudery, the twin sister of narcissism, is another cause of frigidity. Sex, to a prudish wife, is simply a "necessary evil."

A patient who had been married seven years, and suffered from *frigidity*, never undressed in the presence of her husband because "it wasn't nice to appear in the nude."

Another patient whom I interviewed was married twice and still a virgin. She was divorced both times. She claimed she wanted to live in marriage in a platonic relationship. She was prudish during each courtship and surprised each husband by refusing complete sexual relations. On two attempts by the first husband, she developed vaginismus which made penetration practically impossible. She was a very attractive woman twenty-six years of age. She came for a psychiatric interview on the advice of her physician, but stated that she definitely did not wish to change her views about chastity.

Some husbands are so prudish in sexual matters that their wives are afraid to abandon themselves to sex pleasures. They fear their husband's reaction to any display of uninhibited behavior. As a result they repress all signs of sexual cravings. This in itself can cause the wife to become frigid. The husband fails to give his wife the "green light" as it were. Such women may be conscious of a strong urge to let themselves go—to cast all inhibitions to the wind—but they are handicapped by a fear of betraying their secret cravings before the kind of husband who prefers to keep sex *formal*. A *normal* husband should consider himself very fortunate married to a woman who displays evidence of intense passion in the privacy of the bedroom.

Psychiatrists often find it necessary to reeducate the uninformed husband so that the wife can be encouraged not to repress her cravings but to express them without restraint.

One common cause is the repression of the sexual appetite. Some women are under the impression that it is abnormal to enjoy sex. They were brought up to believe

CAUSES OF FRIGIDITY

that anything connected with sex was sordid, that women submitted themselves sexually to husbands as a *duty*. They regard sex hunger as something shameful or sinful. This has been the result of false modesty and neurotic taboos placed on sex facts by their parents. The denial of their sex cravings causes many women to become health-complainers. They have been conditioned in childhood to suppress sexual curiosity.

One patient who complained of being frigid since the day of her marriage made the following significant comments:

"I don't like to undress in front of my husband. He undresses in front of me. I don't like to look at him. I don't enjoy his kisses. His kisses leave me cold. I don't like soul kisses. I don't kiss him during intercourse. I'm frightened because I think I'm undersexed. Even if my husband and I had sex relations every week, I wouldn't take any part in it. I only get a climax when he masturbates me. It's unpleasant when he puts his penis inside of me."

The analysis of her case revealed that she had always been afraid of sex—regarding it as something "evil." She was accused by her boy friends during late adolescence as a "prude." She described her early attitudes toward sex as follows:

"Sex was always a distasteful subject to me. I spent much time in religious schools. My ideas of sex were very high, my knowledge of sex was nil. Outside of a few kisses, I was quite pure. When I was eighteen, I petted with a boy.

I remember I was so ashamed, I ran home and cried. Later he tried to convince me that it wasn't wrong, that it was actually normal. He partially convinced me, and I allowed him the privilege of playing around just to stop him from worrying me so. But it was just 'hand play.' We never had an intercourse. He said I was a prude.

"During my honeymoon intercourse was painful. My husband satisfied me with his hand. This method persisted for one year. A doctor stretched me with instruments but it was still painful. It always hurt throughout our marriage."

Whenever the vagina is dilated and a gynecologist feels there is no longer any reason for any physical discomfort we are inclined to conclude that the pain is "psychic" and represents a psychological hangover from the initial painful coitus during the honeymoon.

"After the birth of my first child, it was easier for my husband to insert his penis but apparently no enjoyment was possible for me. I found all kinds of excuses. I would put it off until I no longer could stand sex relations. Then I would grit my teeth and bear it. I would like to add here that I can't kiss my husband in the mouth and especially not during intercourse. I don't like to. My husband's nudity nauseates me. I have tried to be 'sexy.' But it didn't work. I guess I must be the *frigid type*."

Reeducation in this case was all that was necessary. She learned that there was nothing to be ashamed of in the sex urge; that sexual relations need not be ugly and painful, and that she had nothing to fear or despise in her sexual

CAUSES OF FRIGIDITY

relations with her husband. Soon she found her husband's nakedness no longer repulsive and became normally responsive.

Psychic Traumas

Some women who claim to be sexually unresponsive give a history of having been subjected to an unpleasant sexual experience in early life, which accounts for their aversion to sex. A girl may relate how at the age of twelve she was fondled sexually by her uncle. In some instances a girl is seduced by her own brother. Teen-age girls who have been made pregnant and have had to undergo an abortion often develop an attitude of repulsion toward sex and long after marriage are unable to forget the psychological injury (psychic trauma) to their love life.

Men who expose themselves before little girls very often damage the normal development of the girl's sex life. Carelessness on the part of the parents resulting in a child witnessing intercourse also does damage. Parents sometimes are directly responsible for the development of frigidity in their daughters because of misinforming them regarding sexual matters.

These early unfortunate influences tend to disillusion women regarding the beautiful side of sex.

One of the cases of frigidity caused by psychic trauma encountered in clinical practice was that of a college girl,

Roberta, who had developed such a strong repulsion to men physically that she found herself becoming attracted to her own sex.

This girl's father was a farmer, and ever since she could remember he had been careless about dress. He made a practice of going about the house in his underwear, partially exposed before his daughter. Even when she was full-grown, coming home from college on vacation, her father continued to go about half clad. It repulsed her. She wondered continually whether it was just carelessness, or if he was exhibiting himself purposely. To the psychiatrist, cases like these are not always a matter of pure carelessness. The persistence of the practice clearly indicates a subconscious motive of something more than just mere carelessness.

This girl, in talking of her inability to face the idea of marriage, used a classic phrase often heard by the psychiatrist: "Were I to marry, it would be like going to bed with my father." For her to marry, and have relations with her husband, after being mentally conditioned all those years to seeing her own father's sexual organ, would mean that she could not help making some mental comparisons. In such cases, the feeling is bound to arise that any sex act would be equivalent to intercourse with her father.

Fear of pregnancy is often instilled in daughters by mothers who hope to protect them in this way. Mothers should never tell their daughters of the difficult time they had in labor. In cases where a mother is having a child at home, the other children should never be allowed to overhear evidence of labor pains.

An ugly scene or repeated phrase can become so fixed in the mind of a child that in later years the incidence recurs everytime the young man or woman encounters a sex situation. One patient whom I treated for frigidity told me, "When I was a child, my mother told me all men are beasts." Another of my patients wrote during analysis: "When I was twelve years old I ran across a card in my father's drawer with a picture of a nude woman. On the back was an obscene story. I knew I would be punished if I was caught. The picture made a deep impression on me. I was very much ashamed of my father. I often thought of it in later years. When I would think of it, it would be repulsive and disgusting."

When I asked a patient who had been referred to me by her physician because of frigidity if she could remember the earliest sexual recollection in her childhood she related the following:

"I was nine when this happened. We kids had to play in the back. The man upstairs used to send us for cigarettes and give us coupons. One Sunday morning he called me upstairs. When he went to get his money he put his hand under my dress and felt my sex parts. He said, "Little girls are nice,' and petted me on the buttocks. He gave me cigarette coupons. His wife was sick in bed at the time. When I brought them back he asked me to sit on one of his legs. He had his penis out. It was repulsive to me. He talked sweet to me. I wasn't afraid of him but I felt it was wrong. He took off my panties and ran his hand over me. I was excited. His penis was erect. I saw a lot of black hair. That was the most repulsive part. The whole thing was covered with hair. It was a fairly large penis. I told him I had to go. He gave me nine or ten pennies. I had to urinate. I was excited. I didn't know whether to tell mother. I felt guilty. I saw iron rust on my panties. I thought it was blood. I confessed the episode to my aunt. She told me never to go near that man. I told her never to tell mother."

Many wives who claim they find touching their husband's penis repulsive have had such experiences as described above which accounts for their present reaction to the male organ. The shock remains with them for many years. They try to repress it, but repression only causes conflict, a sense of guilt, and eventually, actual physical illness.

Sex Guilt

Submitting to illicit sexual relations may produce frigidity. Conflicts between physical cravings and religious censorship tends to cause states of anxiety which in turn leads to the development of "sexual anesthesia" (absence of sexual feelings).

Exaggerated feelings of guilt in connection with what a woman does or even what she thinks sexually can make her not only frigid but ill. It is not actually what she does

CAUSES OF FRIGIDITY

sexually, but the self-inflicted guilt about what she does that makes her sick. The sex guilt may be entirely unconcious. She may say, "I don't feel guilty about anything I've done." But the physical symptoms that take her to a doctor's office are telling a different story.

One of my patients was a young attractive married woman who complained of an inability to experience an orgasm during sex relations with her husband. When asked to recall those influences and experiences in her life which she thought might have had some bearing on the development of her frigidity she wrote as follows:

"When I was 5 years old I was punished severely for doing what most children do at that age. I was quite interested in other children's bodies. I was caught watching another little girl putting stones in her vagina. I was accused of doing the same thing but I was only watching. At that time I could not comprehend why it was so bad. Instead of an explanation I was punished. It made an impression on my mind that was not good. If an explanation was given and little attention paid to it I believe I would have forgotten it. The *guilt feeling* started as of then. At that same age I started to play with mother's syringe apparatus and put it against my sex parts. It was very pleasurable. I know I felt guilty about it and did it with the fear of being caught but I liked it too well. I eventually stopped of my own accord."

Many parents regard evidences of sexual awakening or sexual curiosity in their children as a bad sign. They avoid embarrassing questions and only enhance their children's guilt when they manifest interest of any kind in sexual matters.

The patient continued her story as follows:

"I remember very little of my life at 6 and 7. I just remember I always had the feeling I was going to do wrong in regards to sex but what, I didn't know. I was watched and always questioned. I always feared my parents when they would question me on something like that. It seemed as though they were afraid I would do something and I had an idea it was with sex but I was quite ignorant of what they were thinking.

"At 8, 9 and 10 I do not believe I thought much about it. At 11 I attempted masturbation when taking a bath. It happened accidentally while washing myself. It felt pleasurable but I made myself stop it. I did not rub myself, but just pressed. I had a very *guilty* feeling about that and told myself I would never attempt that again, although I believe I was tempted but did not yield to it. I felt like I was bad for even doing it. At 12 or 13 I started to develop. I believe it was the beginning of 12. I was completely in the dark about sex and my body. I wanted to know everything then—especially where babies came from. I thought they came out of the navel. I remember I announced one day to my grandmother that I knew where babies came from. She thought it was cute that I did know. She said very little but asked who told me. So I told her. Next thing I knew mother was questioning me again. No explanation was given, and I was told not to think of such things. I was given the impression that it was bad to think of it. That really set my mind going in a circle. I also felt very guilty. I actually didn't know what to do with my mind on the matter as I couldn't stop wondering about it."

From the above it is evident that she need to be enlightened particularly now that she was approaching the age of puberty, an age when children want to know where babies come from. It is around this age also that girls learn to masturbate and develop their first feelings of guilt in connection with the practice.

"By the time I was 15 years old I was fully developed. In fact I thought I was overdeveloped. I weighed about 120 and seemed like I was all breasts. I was proud of them in a way, but I was also ashamed of them. Back when I was 12 and started to develop I remember my mind had been in quite a turmoil about them developing and my questions were never answered and I remember one night I made a vow that I wouldn't pay much attention to my body when I grew up. It was in regard to my breasts. I cannot remember much about my thoughts that night. I know I was alone in my bedroom and my thoughts were about my growing up. I was very confused and very ignorant of things. I thought all my thoughts were bad and that my body was bad."

Had she been given some information by her mother

relative to the elementary facts about sex, she would have been spared the seeds of guilt often responsible for the development of frigidity in adult life.

"From the age of 15 until marriage I never could figure things out on sex. I know my body would react when I kissed a boy and I always felt guilty about it but I also knew I liked it. I didn't know what to do myself. I was still interested in sex but I sure was confused. I grew up but not where sex was concerned. I knew very, very little about it. In fact I have learned about things only after marriage. When going with my husband before marriage my emotions really got out of hand and I felt very guilty about them. I was more confused than I ever had been. I suffered from guilt terribly. When the day came to be married I was in sort of a fog. Everything I did was done mechanically.

"I realize now that my sexual frigidity started in childhood because of my ignorance. If I had had explanations I would have come out fine. I also wanted attention from boys and the way I got it was by pretending I was *coldnatured* when I was not. As far back as I can remember I was always attracted to the opposite sex.

"I could never understand my mother and I feared her all my life. She would never let me make decisions. She made them for me. She never taught me properly on sex, probably she didn't know how. I believe she transmitted to me her own thoughts about sex. The impression I have of her opinion on sex is *disgust*. Although I could never quite get myself to be disgusted with it, I always experienced guilt feelings."

The above case illustrates the cause for her inability to enjoy sex relations with her husband. Her association of sex during childhood and adolescence was that it was bad. These guilt feelings were responsible for her inhibitions—her deep-seated fear of allowing herself the necessary abandonment for the achievement of an orgasm.

A young divorcée had been referred to me because of symptoms which her physician believed to be "psychosomatic" in nature. She complained of malaise, loss of appetite and depressed spells. Her husband had divorced her because she was *frigid* and had rejected him too many times sexually.

Upon inquiring into her sex life, she related the following:

"My chief emotional complaint is a feeling of *guilt*, the manifestations of which are countless. The most devastating result of this feeling is its effect on my sexual capacities. It's a constant struggle to keep guilt feelings from inhibiting the performance. I can't seem to get an orgasm from intercourse. I feel tormented and hostile.

"I married because I was pregnant. I resented the whole situation. I never got an orgasm. I never felt the need for sex. I was never aroused and was never passionate before marriage. I resented the role of motherhood. My husband drank to excess. It made our sex relations worse. He accused me of being 'cold.' He very seldom gave me any preliminary sex play. I never liked to see my husband undressed."

I have found that frigidity is quite common among women who married because they were pregnant at the time of the ceremony. It appears that these women carry their guilt feelings into their marriage.

Penis-Envy

The term refers to the psychoanalytic concept that women unconsciously wish they had been born with a male sex organ. According to the Freudian hypothesis, women feel they have been cheated or deprived of that which the male sex possessed, namely the penis, and consequently they envy men.

This underlying wish to have a penis expresses itself in disguised ways—women find themselves competing with men, or they become what Adler describes as "masculine-protest" types, aggressive and dominating. It explains the so-called "masculinity complex" in women—the renunciation of femininity and passivity. It accounts for a certain type of *frigidity*—wherein women have their sensations highly localized in the clitoris and experience very little satisfaction from actual intercourse.

Some psychoanalysts attribute many of the neurotic symptoms in women to this lack of a penis which fact plays an important role in the development of a woman's personality.

This concept of penis-envy is based on the principle that when a girl sees the masculine organ for the first time, she suffers a "psychic trauma" insofar as she wonders why she too was not born with a similar appendage and develops as a consequence feelings of envy.

One of my women patients offered the following comments regarding her fantasies of wanting to possess a male organ: "When I masturbate it is the clitoris which I understand is equivalent of the penis. I have never allowed an orgasm except through the clitoris because I reject the feminine role and maintain the clitoris-penis under all circumstances. When having fantasies of heterosexual intercourse, I realize now that I was the man and gained excitement through thinking of a man and a woman having intercourse because I wanted a male organ so that I could have the woman. In allowing a man's penis against my clitoris I am gaining satisfaction of having a penis. My refusal of his organ in my vagina is because that would take my penis (clitoris) away and make me a woman."

Frigidity is related to the penis-envy complex in women insofar as there is a denial of the role of the vagina. However, there are many psychoanalysts who do not subscribe entirely to this theory as it does not apply in all cases. It does hold true in those cases where there is a definite fixation of sexuality on the clitoris and sufficient evidence of masculinity to account for the absence of sexual feelings in the vagina.

Fears and Complexes

Frigidity may arise from the early relationship of the woman to her parents. These relationships may involve what psychoanalysts refer to as a fixation to one's mother or father resulting in a "Mother Complex" or "Father Complex." A woman may have had such a strong attachment to her father (called an "Electra Complex") that she is unable to respond to a man because he is too unlike her father. Or she may be so attached to her mother that she is unable to develop a normal relationship to any man. If she hated her father she may develop an antipathy toward all men.

Certain obsessive fears impede the enjoyment of sex; such fears as a fear of pregnancy, venereal diseases, pain, childbirth, etc.

One husband told me that his wife insisted that he take a bath every time he approached her sexually. She had a complex about the sex act and was obsessed by the idea that unless her husband was thoroughly bathed prior to intercourse she might become infected. The husband's tolerance was exhausted when he learned that despite this ritualistic precoital bathing on his part, she did not respond

CAUSES OF FRIGIDITY

to the point of achieving a climax. She was too preoccupied with her complex to concentrate adequately on the enjoyment of the sex act.

Many women insist on having intercourse with the lights turned out. When the husband does succeed in having intercourse with a wife who comes under this category, he notices that she is unable to relax and manifests evidence of being shy and inhibited. One such wife stated that she did not wish to see her husband's penis as it made her turn against sex. Such complexes are hangovers from a premarital conditioning to the idea that sex is something shameful, and that sexual activities should be carried out only in the dark. Strangely enough there are wives who, despite the fact that they have been married many years, still blush when their husbands attempt to make love to them in the daylight. Some husbands have told me that they have never seen their wives undress in their presence. This false modesty complex is quite common.

There are numerous other fears which interfere with a woman's enjoyment of the sex act, such as fear of contracting a venereal disease, fear of being seen or heard during intercourse, fear of being considered licentious and sensual.

Complexes that interfere with the achievement of an orgasm may involve feelings of guilt, hatred, jealousy, distrust inferiority and other negative emotions. These fears and complexes are more apt to occur among women who are neurotically maladjusted by reason of neurotic influences and experiences in early childhood and adolescence.

Frigidity associated with a fear of pregnancy and childbirth is extremely common. The woman is detracted from the enjoyment of sex relations with her husband because of her preoccupation with neurotic thoughts regarding what might happen to her during childbirth. Many of these women have heard wierd tales about mothers who have died enroute to the hospital, of women screaming with pain on maternity wards in hospitals, and of others who suffered miscarriages accompanied by severe complications.

The mother of five children stated quite frankly that she became frigid following the birth of her second child. She told her husband that she did not want any more children, as their economic status prevented them from caring for them adequately. However, he ignored her pleas and subjected her to subsequent pregnancies. While she did not refuse him sex relations, during each intercourse she would pray that she would not become pregnant. The fear of becoming pregnant during the sex act naturally kept her from having an orgasm.

One of my patients, a very attractive woman who had been married for a period of five years, refused to have her husband complete the sex act even though he took precautions by wearing a contraceptive. During each intercourse she became tense and rigid, fearing that she would become pregnant. She informed me that an aunt of hers had died at childbirth, and she developed the obsession

CAUSES OF FRIGIDITY

that she too might not survive the ordeal. Her husband had her examined by several reputable gynecologists who tried to assure her that she could have a child without having to suffer any labor pains whatsoever. They pointed out that there were some women who could not even recall having experienced any discomfort whatever in connection with the birth of their child. They also found, upon examination, nothing to justify her complaint to her husband that intercourse was painful. They concluded that it was a case of vaginismus due to her inability to relax and enjoy sex.

In this particular case, no amount of assurance from the specialists solved the problem. It required a long series of analytic sessions before she developed sufficient insight as to the root cause of her fears. She discovered that she was using her fear of childbirth as an alibi to excuse her fear of responsibility associated with the bringing-up of a child. She also expressed apprehension that a child might act as a wedge in a love relationship between herself and her husband, and that she would be deprived of certain liberties she was accustomed to. The combination of the insight which she acquired and the discipline she began to exercise in cooperating for the first time during the sex act, enabled her to respond favorably to intercourse.

The fear of pregnancy becomes a greater problem among unmarried women. It is readily understandable how a woman, thinking of the consequences of a pregnancy out of wedlock would be unable to reach a climax.

Many women suffer from breast complexes which interfere with their enjoyment of the sex act. A woman who is flat-chested may be so selfconscious because of her absence of developed breasts that she is unable to respond adequately to sexual intercourse. Other women who have large pendulous breasts suffer from inferiority feelings and are reluctant to appear in the nude before their husbands. Women who resort to the wearing of "falsies" also suffer from a breast inferiority complex. Such breast complexes have been found to deter a woman's enjoyment of the sex act and often contribute to her frigidity.

Many girls become sex-conscious during early adolescense as soon as they become aware of their breasts developing and being noticed by the boys. This breast consciousness is often enhanced by prudish mothers who make the mistake of telling their daughters that they should not attract attention to their breasts by wearing sweaters or brassieres which accentuate the breasts. One patient related how she tried to wrap a piece of cloth tightly around her chest so that her breasts would be unnoticeable. She associated the development of her breasts with something to be ashamed of. She feared that people would accuse her of fondling her breasts in order to make them larger. This breast complex which she developed accounted for her inhibitions following marriage to the extent that she was unable to achieve a vaginal orgasm during intercourse. She had been afraid to allow herself to enjoy mammillary stimulation as a preliminary to intercourse.

Another patient, in being asked to relate when she first became breast conscious, wrote the following:

"When I first started to grow, I remember how proud I was of the two little swelling nipples of my breasts. I would secretly look at them, yet wanted to slump and hide when I was around people, for fear they were showing through my dress. I was also very embarrassed in front of my mother. Later on, all my girl friends were wearing brassieres and I didn't have one. I kept wondering if my mother would mention it and get one for me but she never did. I was sixteen and working already when one day the girls at work started teasing me about 'bouncing' when I walked. I felt ashamed. My girl friend couldn't understand why my mother hadn't purchased a brassiere for me as her mother had told her to get a 'bra' after she had developed some. This girl friend took me shopping with her. I wasn't very large and the salesgirl couldn't find a brassiere to fit me very well—which added to my embarrassment. I remember wearing it for weeks and hiding it at home. This must happen to many girls. I know many girls who try to hide them."

Another patient told how some men at work sent one of the stenographers, who was flat-chested, a pair of "falsies." Such innocent pranks are often responsible for the development of serious emotional conflicts that lead to frigidity and a turning away from all men.

One husband compared his wife's breasts to two "fried eggs" which of course gave her a deep sense of physical inferiority and interfered with her enjoyment of sex. She frankly confessed that she disliked undressing in front of her husband.

Some women do not like to have men touch their breasts. This also acts as a handicap as most women enjoy having their breasts fondled and kissed. It arouses in them a desire for intercourse.

A patient who confessed to frigidity admitted that she never permitted her husband to manipulate her breasts. When she learned that breast-sucking was normal she decided to experiment as she wanted to overcome her frigidity. This was the first step toward overcoming her inhibitions. She was ultimately able to abandon herself to her husband's lovemaking and began experiencing coital orgasms.

Another patient was so upset because of hair growing around her nipples that she developed a complex about being kissed on her breasts. When the hair was removed by electrolysis it improved her response to sexual foreplay.

Masturbation

Masturbation plays an important role in the development of frigidity among women. Many women who are unable to enjoy a coital orgasm claim that their sensations of highest sexual excitability are localized in the clitoris. In some in-

CAUSES OF FRIGIDITY

stances this develops as a result of excessive digital stimulation of the clitoris.

Wives who are sexually unsatisfied are apt to masturbate as a substitute form of sex gratification. The fixation of their sexuality to the clitoris contributes to their inability to achieve a vaginal orgasm during coitus.

Because of a fear of hurting themselves by introducing objects into the vagina which might result in a tearing of the hymen, many adolescent girls prefer to stimulate or rub their clitoris and masturbate in this way. In bathing their sex parts with a cloth or allowing a stream of water to flow against the clitoris they learn that they are able to bring about an orgasm.

Some husbands satisfy their wives by producing an orgasm via the rubbing of the clitoris with their hand which tends to make it more difficult for the wives to ultimately attain an orgasm from coitus.

In this respect girls who masturbate, achieving an orgasm by introducing some object as a penis-substitute into their vagina, have an advantage over those who manipulate the clitoris. They are less apt to develop frigidity as they are preparing the vagina for more voluptuous sensations when they have intercourse for the first time.

Many wives are frigid because of past masturbation conflicts. They harbor the misconception that they have harmed themselves by having masturbated during their adolescent years. Their feelings of guilt associated with the practice interfere with the attainment of an orgasm during coitus.

These guilt feelings leave scars that jeopardize the chances for sexual happiness. When the sense of shame is cast off through enlightenment, the first step has been taken to achieve sexual compatibility.

A patient who had never experienced a vaginal orgasm with her husband, confessed to having masturbated to excess prior to marriage. She felt her frigidity was God's punishment for her sexual sin. She even feared she would go insane unless she stopped.

Regarding her sexual difficulties, she wrote:

"Everytime my husband had intercourse with me, I'd cry my eyes out because I couldn't get any feeling. I never had an orgasm from intercourse. The only way I get a climax is to rub my clitoris.

"When I masturbate I believe I am doing myself harm. I would rub the nipples of my breasts to arouse myself. I've masturbated three or four times a week, having all sorts of fantasies about wild parties. I dream of other men making love to me." (psychic infidelity)

She responded favorably to psychiatric treatment now that her conflicts involving masturbation were eliminated. Both husband and wife were given a lecture course in sex technique.

Women who are left sexually unsatisfied by their husbands very often resort to masturbation as an outlet for their pent-up sexual energy. Being gratified via masturbation (which one's husband knows nothing about) they naturally become disinterested in sex relations and are often accused of being "cold."

Narcissism.

Many beautiful women suffer from frigidity—finding it difficult to experience an orgasm during sexual relations because of what psychiatrists refer to as narcissism. They possess too much self-love and as a consequence are unable to establish a normal love relationship with another person. Literally speaking these women are married to their faces. Their sexual hunger (libido) is transferred from the genitals to the love of themselves. They wish to be admired and loved but do not wish to *give* love. Allowing for exceptions of course, many beautiful women have an unconscious desire to attract or *tease* many men but refuse to fall in love with any one man. Many of them are unable to accept sex and are *frigid* because, *unconsciously*, sex to them detracts from their beauty—as if to say they are too beautiful for what they consider "sordid." They are like statues—as the French say "filles de marbres" (daughters of marble)—only to be admired.

I once interviewed a beautiful woman who had been married three times and had never been "deflowered." She was divorced by each of three husbands. She harbored a conscious antipathy toward all men. The analysis of this case showed that she suffered from a strong narcissistic component. She possessed too much self-love to be able to "give" herself to any man.

Promiscuity

Many women are frigid because of promiscuity. By promiscuity we mean sexual relations with a frequent change of sexual partners. The term implies giving onself sexually to a person independent of any feeling of love. The tendency to become sexually intimate indiscriminately with or without remuneration of some kind may be considered symptomatic of a prostitution complex.

An unfaithful wife—one who is promiscuous—may make comparisons in love technique with her husband who fails to satisfy her. She sometimes receives gifts from her many male friends and looks forward to more gifts. These hard-pressed and frustrated wives may be drawn into further love affairs for the sake of the gifts. Soon, she enjoys the privilege of accepting man's sexual advances only if she is remunerated. According to Jassny's theory, the so-called "procuress" despises her own sex and assumes a pseudo-masculine attitude by attempting to imitate a man in the same capacity. In reality she ridicules the man who is obligated to pay for his gratification. Through promiscuity or prostitution, "a circuitous path to masculinity," woman

CAUSES OF FRIGIDITY

rebels against man by subjugating him to the state of sexual slavery. The more primitive her clients become in the expression of their sexuality, the greater becomes her repugnance for men in general.

Women who become professional prostitutes suffer from various forms of frigidity. They are considered by psychoanalysts as unconscious homosexuals—lesbians, who take flight to many men in order to run away from homosexuality. It explains why most of them are unable to experience a sexual climax during intercourse even when they are with a male friend they like.

One of my patients was a young woman, slender, in her late twenties, who never married and complained of never having reached a climax during intercourse with the many men she slept with at different times. She was under the impression that women who are frigid eventually "lose their minds." Despite the guilt she had regarding her promiscuous relations with numerous men, she found it difficult to change—that is "to refuse men" as she put it.

Although she drank to excess and admitted that she was less inhibited under the influence of alcoholic beverages, she was still unable to attain a climax even when she was with a man she liked. "I can't get a thrill out of any man," she told me. "When a man puts his penis inside of me I feel 'dead' there." She continued as follows:

"Once I let two fellows play with me at the same time. I even asked several men to have intercourse with me. I wanted to find out if they could make me experience a climax. I tried to enjoy it but I couldn't.

"Nothing ever excites me. Life is *nothing*. I often wonder why I was born. I have no purpose in life. I go out with all sorts of men because I'm *lonesome*. I used to be afraid I would commit suicide sometime when I was drunk.

"Men now repulse me. I don't like to touch their penis. I don't even like the thought of it. A girl friend once told me I was oversexed."

This patient apparently was trying to overcompensate for her deep-seated feelings of inferiority by giving herself to many men. This tended to boost her ego as if to say "Most men want to have intercourse with a girl and if I give myself freely I'll have no trouble getting dates." She had always considered herself unattractive, a poor dancer, unable to converse intelligently, had undeveloped breasts and a protruding chin. Many girls become prostitutes because of their inability to adjust to their inferiorities.

This woman wanted to enjoy sex but her sense of guilt prevented her from attaining an orgasm.

The greater the insecurity in a person, the greater the tendency to indulge in sexual excesses. The same holds true for the excessive intake of food. People who are immature often become fat (oral pleasure). Frustrations in childhood often lead to excessive masturbation. Promiscuity in itself is a form of emotional immaturity. It represents the seeking of "many loves" because of some deep or unconscious feeling of *frustration*.

Sexual Aberrations

Many couples suffer from sexual incompatibility because they are either uninformed or misinformed regarding what is normal and what is abnormal in sex. Because of this problem, wives are often accused of being sexually cold.

Sometimes frigidity is caused by the husband subjecting his wife to an act (such as mouth-genital contact) which she regards as a "perversion." It is understandable that a wife who is completely uninformed in the matter of variations in sexual expression will suffer a shock when she is subjected to any act which offends her aesthetic senses. One patient confessed that she could no longer experience an orgasm during intercourse because her husband once insisted on inserting his penis into her rectum. The physical pain connected with this experience left such a distasteful impression that she was unable to forget the association of sex with the painful experience.

Some of my women patients have admitted that their whole attitude towards sex changed following an isolated instance of an unpleasant experience. The husband who, for example, completes the act of fellatio (ejaculates into his wife's mouth) without preparing her for it may be responsible for the development of reactions of disgust towards the entire sex act.

I have had several husbands tell me that their wives preferred gratification by methods other than intercourse. Indeed, one woman, who was unable to experience an orgasm during intercourse with her husband, sued him for divorce because he refused to perform cunnilingus on her.

If the variation in expression serves as foreplay to the sex act, it is included within the range of normality. But if the particular deviation (fellatio, cunnilingus, stimulation of the clitoris, rectal intercourse, etc.) becomes an end in itself, then it will interfere with one's ability to experience an orgasm from coitus, and is not considered normal. Many husbands who become addicted to sexual aberrations often lose their erection when they attempt intercourse. By the same token, women who *prefer* mouth or digital stimulation of the clitoris often experience reactions of *frigidity* when their husbands insert their penis into the vagina.

One of my patients was a young woman aged 28, married, and the mother of two children. She had asked her physician for the name of a psychiatrist, as she felt she had a personal problem which she could not discuss with anyone else. During her first interview she found it very difficult to express herself, appeared shy and inhibited, and declared that she was too self-conscious to be able to describe her problem.

She said that she felt guilty because she had indulged in sexual activities with her husband which she regarded as abnormal. She worried about this until she was unable to sleep, and came to the conclusion that unless she contacted a psychiatrist she would lose her mind. She was made to feel at ease, and finally informed me that the only way that she achieved a sexual orgasm was to have her husband spank her violently on her buttocks with the back of a hair brush.

She was devoutly religious and entertained sex fantasies of a bizarre nature. She would pray for forgiveness and do penance by repeating certain prayers. It was quite obvious after listening to her other complaints that here was a case of obsessive-compulsion neurosis.

Regarding her desire for flagellation she stated:

"My mind is always occupied with thoughts of being spanked. I beg my husband to spank me. I like to lift my gown and put myself across my husband's legs and then ask my husband to spank me with a brush. He sometimes uses his hands. After four of five minutes I am able to have a sexual climax from the pain which I feel. When he has sexual intercourse with me I have to have fantasies of spanking in order to enjoy it."

This deviation can be traced to earlier episodes of spanking in her life during which she experienced erotic sensations in her sexual organs. She recalled the following incident which took place at the age of ten:

"My sister and I would make a tent with the rug that was hanging over the clothes line. She was 11 years old at the time. We would spank each other with our hands. We would get over each other's knees and slip our pants down and spank each other. That went on for a month. We would take turns. Sometimes we would do it four times in succession. When we were 15 we would tickle each other. I often got over my sister's knees, hoping that she would spank me. She would hit me once or twice. I used to say, 'I'll bet you can't spank me.' That happened five or six times. Those were the only episodes of spanking during my childhood."

It is rather significant that when she was 16 years of age she was asked by her brother-in-law what she wanted for a birthday gift, and she requested that she be slapped 16 times across her buttocks. She remembers that is was pleasurable, because she told him to spank her quite hard. She entertained fantasies of being raped by men. Her bisexual conflict is evidenced by the statement that she sometimes would see a woman and thought she had turned into a man. She once wished that she could become a hobo, take her dog with her and travel on railroad trains and dress in men's clothes. She even entertained bizarre fantasies of wondering what it would taste like to bite a dog. During late adolescence she would become nervous looking at pictures in magazines of nude women (a defense against latent homosexuality). She felt compelled to turn the page, lest her finger would accidentally come in touch with the sex region in the picture. She would walk past the burlesque theater and would hold her breath, fearing she would become contaminated by the sin she felt at the time, and would then expectorate. She felt guilty to breathe as she walked by the theater. She reacted the same way whenever she saw dog feces on the street.

Some of her fantasies are homosexual in nature. She became panicky on one occasion because she wanted a certain woman to spank her and was afraid she might approach her.

She gets sexual excitement from hitting her dog, but gets a choking feeling in her throat after she does it. She enjoys thinking of two men spanking each other. This can be interpreted as disguised evidence of her own homosexual desires. She once thought of being tied down to an ironing board while a man spanked her. She often wished that she had become a nun, as she felt it would have kept her from indulging in masturbation. During adult life she enjoyed masturbating by lifting her dress, pulling her pants down, and hitting herself with a stick or her hand. This was sexually very exciting to her, and would last about five minutes at a time. It was the only way she could achieve an orgasm. During intercourse with her husband she sometimes imagined being in jail and having the woman matron in charge hit her over the buttocks with a whip. When she spanked her sister's child it gave her a sexual thrill. She enjoyed looking in the mirror to examine the red marks on her buttocks. When she worked, she would cross her legs and move them in a certain way in order to experience a sexual thrill.

As previously mentioned, this case involved a young married woman who was unable to achieve an orgasm during coitus with her husband. Analysis brought out the apparent root-cause of this orgasm-incapacity. Her libido had been anchored to a deviation which was traced to her early childhood. She had been spanked at the age of six by her mother, and during those same early years her father would threaten to use his strap on her. She began entertaining fantasies of what it would feel like to be strapped by her father. At the age of ten she and her sister spanked each other and she noticed that she experienced pleasurable sensations in her genitals. She became conditioned to this masochistic method of sexual gratification and soon developed symptoms of an obsessive-compulsive neurosis. She states that she reached a climax and has since entertained fantasies of being fondled and spanked by her father. She soon developed symptoms of an obsessive-compulsive neurosis as described throughout the case.

Her father wanted her to be a boy and even gave her a boy's name. She became aware of her father's displeasure at her being a girl and tried to please him by becoming tomboyish. She was very attached to her father and the evidence reveals the formation of a father fixation. Her neurosis was a defense reaction to the guilt she felt associated with her repressed incestuous fixation to her father. The latent homosexual component manifested itself via anxiety whenever she slept with her own sex, and her fantasies of two women spanking each other. The spanking can be intrepreted as a masochistic need to be punished for sexual thoughts in church which she regards as sacriligious. This also applies to her frigidity with her husband. In other words, she unconsciously considers it a sin to experience an orgasm with her husband as it would be equivalent to enjoying an incestuous intercourse with her father. She even stated that she would hold her body rigid and enjoyed this. To be rigid means to be inhibited—not to move during coitus. The conflict is so acute that she compromises via the development of her compulsion neurosis.

She tries to relive in her adult life experiences which gave her pleasure in her younger years (regression to childhood). All deviations are a regression to the polymorphous perverse stage of sexual development.

We see the development of her sexual neurosis arising out of an early relationship to her father. The sexual impulse is unable to attach itself to a love-object (her husband) because it is anchored to an "Electra complex."

Not being able to understand the mechanisms involved in her deviation, prior to analysis she was unable to resist the cravings of her perverse sexual instinct. However as soon as she was able to appreciate the interpretation of her flagellation complex as a need for punishment because of her incestuous desires for her father, she gradually lost the desire to be spanked. She stated that she found coitus with her husband more satisfying and she no longer found the need to masturbate. She stopped her flagellation activities. Four years have elapsed since termination of treatment.

Bedroom Mistakes: Faulty Technique

Frigidity, in many instances, is the symptom-consequences of errors in lovemaking technique.

Bad judgment, for example, on the part of the husband

in choosing a time for lovemaking can cause a wife to become frigid.

Occasionally, the husband will awaken at two o'clock in the morning and decide he wants relations with his wife. He awakens her abruptly, when she is sleepy and not in a responsive mood, and frigidity ensues. Very few women are in the mood for sex in the morning when they are thinking of the day's task ahead. Husbands who demand sex relations of their wives at these odd hours haven't thought the situation out well. They are sacrificing a finer relationship for a momentary gratification.

Those husbands who subject their wives to sexual excesses, who insist on having intercourse every night or every other night or two or three times in one day, fail to realize that they are sowing the seeds of frigidity in their wives.

Many wives have been brought up in the old-fashioned tradition that a husband's marital rights should never be questioned. They feel it is the wife's *duty* to submit at all times to the husband's desires. This constitutes neurotic martyrdom and usually kills the wife's response in the long run.

One wife who came to me told me that her husband wanted sex relations at all hours of the night with tiring frequency. She submitted, feeling it to be her duty whether she was in the "mood" for love or not. Gradually, the bad association of too many unhappy times with her husband made her completely *frigid*. She reached the point where she could not stand the sight of her husband.

This is not a rare case by any means. To a lesser degree, many wives harbor the same resentment because their husbands have ridden roughshod over their feelings in the matter.

I have encountered numerous husbands who harbor the fallacy that women enjoy being abused on the theory that they are masochists, and enjoy being subjected to sexual practices against their will. Such husbands who are compelled to call their wives profane names prior to or during the sex act, or abuse them physically, very often suffer from "psychic impotence." The sadistic abuse of their wives is a necessary requirement for the attainment of an adequate erection. Abusiveness on the part of the husband invariably causes the disillusioned wife to become frigid.

Every psychiatrist has heard husbands complain, "My wife is always tired. She never wants sex." This may indicate neurotic fatigue. The wife who is *always* tired is actually bored. She is using the excuse to get out of sex relations with her husband because she no longer feels love and physical desire for him. For the health and happiness of both, this situation should never be allowed to drag on.

If a husband feels that his wife really is fatigued from her day's work, he should tell her to go to bed early, rest and relax, and they will enjoy their relationship more. If at the end of a rest period, she still rejects him, he has good reason to wonder if it is true fatigue or an escape.

Husbands are often baffled when wives use the excuse that they are too exhausted from housework to have sex.

Yet the same wife will work at her ironing or mending until late at night. He asks, "If you're so tired, why do you keep on working—why don't you get to bed?"

She will say, "But I *have* to get this done." What she means is that she has to keep on with the housework because consciously or unconsciously, it is her way out of physical relations with her husband. It is the same story with the husband who has to bring work home from the office every night.

If either partner is up against this situation, it is time for an investigation. Resentment and quarreling over the giving or the not giving of love only produces impotence reactions in the husband and *frigidity* in the wife. Husband and wife should talk it over in an intelligent way, and if the marriage continues cold, both should seek the guidance of a psychiatrist. They need to find out why their physical union—which should be a steady source of happiness—has broken down.

Many of these situations would not arise and persist if there were more frankness between husband and wife about being in the "mood" for love. I am often surprised by the indirect ways that a husband or wife will notify the partner of a feeling of desire. Instead of realizing that it is a happy circumstance, husbands and wives carry over an adolescent shyness into marriage and are ashamed to tell each other of their feelings.

The result is often confusion and a succession of disappointments. One husband told me, "I never know when

CAUSES OF FRIGIDITY   141

my wife wants me. Sometimes she will be affectionate when we have gone to bed, but if I try to make love to her, she will "freeze up," get angry and push me away. Other times when she acts affectionately, she accepts me."

It is a *mistake* to omit preliminary love-play which should be gracefully and artfully performed. In good dramatic plays, the first act sets the mood and prepares for the dramatic climax. If it is awkward and unappealing, the audience is unmoved, and the ending leaves no afterglow.

If the husband is nervous and excitable, inadequate and *hasty* in lovemaking, he may have a quick satisfaction and make the error of not allowing sufficient time for his wife to respond. According to one investigator, forty percent of wives estimated that intercourse lasted less than five minutes; most women require a much longer time to be sufficiently aroused. The frustrated wife should recognize that premature satisfaction on her husband's part is a sexual disorder and she should advise him to do something about it. When the husband's technique is bad and there is no improvement, the wife should refer him to a psychiatrist. The condition he suffers from will not cure itself. Premature ejaculation on the part of husbands is the cause of frigidity among many wives.

A young woman who had been married approximately four months consulted me regarding her inability to achieve a sexual climax during sex relations with her husband. At first she felt guilty and thought perhaps that she had not been cooperating during the sex act. However, upon investigation it was learned that her husband who was ignorant in sexual matters had failed to use adequate technique. He did nothing in the way of attempting to arouse her sexually prior to coitus. There was an absence of any preliminary loveplay. His approach was very unromantic and following the insertion of his penis it required a few seconds for him to ejaculate, leaving his wife totally unsatisfied. His wife knew it wasn't intelligent for them to go on being sexually incompatible without seeking advice so she decided to consult with her family doctor who in turn referred her to me.

She related her sexual difficulties to me in the following manner:

"I never had an orgasm since I've been married. My husband is very sensitive. If I touch his penis with my hand he ejaculates. When he places his penis inside of me, he never waits for me. At first I thought I was to blame. Not being satisfied made me very nervous. I've cried many times thinking we would never be happy. I heard about frigidity and thought maybe I could never get a climax."

In later sessions she went on to say:

"My husband seldom kisses me during the sex act. He places his full weight on me so that I can hardly breathe. He's awkward and doesn't take his time."

It was necessary in this case to enlist the cooperation of the husband. His premature ejaculation was the result of an anxiety neurosis which responded favorably to psychotherapy.

His technique improved immeasurably and the wife began to experience orgasms from the sex act which made her extremely happy.

Women today in increasing numbers admit and ask help for their own lack of sexual response. In many cases, their frigidity is caused by clumsy or inadequate lovemaking on the part of the husband. Very few women want to remain unresponsive—most want to respond, want to love and be loved. They are eager to learn ways of overcoming their inability to respond.

It is a *mistake* for a wife to hate her husband because he is a clumsy lover. He will hate back. It is better to do something constructive—to seek help. Sexual harmony in the early years of marriage will mean a better relationship in later years.

Many women are *afraid* to enjoy the sex act. They fear exhibiting passion in the bedroom, thinking their husbands may be *shocked* by their lack of inhibitions.

Other women make the serious mistake of engaging in distracting activities during the sex act. One husband complained that his wife was so unresponsive that she continued reading her book while he had intercourse with her. Another told me his wife kept on applying nail polish to her finger nails during the sex act rather than be interrupted in what she was doing. These bedroom mistakes sound fantastic but psychiatrists are not surprised to hear the many ways in which some wives manifest their frigidity or indifference to sexual lovemaking.

For women to display false modesty in the bedroom is decidedly an error in technique. One man complained that his wife always insisted that the lights be turned out during sex relations. When he tried to explain to her that sexual intimacies between husband and wife were natural and nothing to be ashamed of, she still preferred to adhere to her prudish demands stating that she felt embarrassed and uncomfortable. I generally make it a point to convince such women that neuroticism of this kind is proof of their *immaturity* and that it is unintelligent for them to behave like a "child wife" in the bedroom. Incidentally, wives are more apt to accept the advice of a psychiatrist than to listen to the same advice from the husband.

A woman should not make the error of going to bed looking her worst. No husband enjoys making love to his wife when her head is covered with metal curlers or her face smeared with cold cream. The wife who bathes, combs her hair, applies a drop or two of perfume and puts on a fetching nightgown knows the wisdom of bedroom stimulation in order to keep her husband on the straight and narrow path. There must be a reason why magazines advertise black lace negligees that are supposed to be stimulating to the eye. They caution wives not to lose sex appeal.

Mistakes in technique on the part of wives tend to frustrate husbands who in turn develop impotence reactions as a result of which wives are left sexually unsatisfied.

For the highest mutual attraction couples should avoid saying or doing anything in the bedroom which will tend to diminish or take away the pleasure one should derive from the sex act.

Husbands should be imaginative and not resort to the same routine technique year in and year out. The monotony of the same approach on the part of the husband can cause the wife to become unresponsive. An occasional different technique adds renewed interest to the art of lovemaking.

Neither the husband nor wife should suspect that their partner has acquired knowledge of any new sex technique via the extramarital route. Rather, each should look upon it as a desire of the other to extend this phase of their marriage and increase the pleasure both can derive from the sexual relationship.

Bedroom Mistakes: The Castration Mechanism

As a result of the interrelationship between the mind and the sex parts there is a phenomenon which psychoanalysts refer to as "Psychic Castration." Both sexes should be acquainted with this mechanism as it plays an important role in the development of impotence in men and frigidity in women.

Few women realize that men are *sexually sensitive*—capable of losing a desire for sex relations in a matter of minutes. The penis may be merely an appendage of flesh but it has a "soul" as it were. When insulted it behaves accordingly.

For example, when a wife, in the middle of sex relations, exclaims: "By the way, did you mail my letter?" or "Did you lock the back door?" she is literally desexing or *castrating* her husband. He becomes frustrated, loses his erection and the lovemaking becomes a fiasco.

Frigid wives are more apt to be guilty of castrating their husbands. They generally make such remarks as "If you insist on having sex relations, hurry up and get it over with," or "Must we do *that* again?" These women apparently fail to realize that a *cutting* remark can feel like a knife on the penis.

There are many examples of ways in which women defeat their own purpose. They become their own enemies. Women are dependent upon men not only for material security but are emotionally dependent in the sense that they want to be loved, respected and treated with kindness by the male sex. Abusing a husband makes him less desirous of sex. Physical closeness between husband and wife is essential to happiness in marriage.

When a wife castrates her husband either through nagging, bringing up the unpleasant past, rejecting him or insulting him, she reminds me of a woman sitting on the limb of a tree and sawing it off, overlooking the fact that she is sitting on the part that is being sawed off. Many frigid wives have been responsible for the husbands going on a "sexual strike." They go months without approaching their wives sexually because of something she said or has done to kill his interest in her.

CAUSES OF FRIGIDITY

One man once told me he attended a party with his wife. A young, attractive young woman came over and sat on his lap in a playful sort of way. The wife was furious and gave vent to her jealousy and anger by slapping her husband across the face, creating a scene and spoiling the evening for everyone. After weeks of no conversation between husband and wife, the wife finally broke down, apologized for her actions and asked to be forgiven. The husband attempted to forget the entire episode but when he tried to resume sex relations with her, he experienced an inability to perform. His impotence was no doubt the result of being psychically castrated by his wife. He tried to regain his potency but failed. Finally in desperation he divorced his wife and married some other woman with whom he was sexually potent. His former wife never remarried and still regrets her costly mistake.

Belittling a husband, causing him embarrassment, reminding him of his deficiencies *desexualizes* a man. I caution wives against this neurotic method of dealing with a difficult husband. It makes the situation worse.

Castration or desexualization doesn't always come as a result of being frustrated by a frigid woman. It can come about from influences within. When this happens it is spoken of as *autocastration.* A husband may feel guilty for having cheated on his wife and may decide quite unconsciously to punish himself by no longer being able to perform sexually with his wife. As a consequence, the wife is left *sexually unsatisfied* and never learns the real source of her husband's sudden impotence. Or a man may be potent with his wife and when he attempts to engage in an extramarital affair he notices that he is unable to sustain his erection. His guilt causes him to become impotent, which also comes under the phenomenon of autocastration.

Castration, in the broad sense of the term, applies to women as well if we speak of castration as any influence or factor which comes from within or without capable of traumatizing our sexual urge. We could say that a woman who is unable to achieve a vaginal orgasm during intercourse with her husband because of some unconscious guilt, is a victim of autocastration. Frigidity in many instances is self-imposed.

Women who harbor strong feelings of hostility toward men often punish themselves because of guilt associated with hatred by depriving themselves of sex enjoyment.

Sometimes a wife will *castrate* her husband by making an uncalled-for remark or deliberately insulting him, and feel guilty afterwards. When the husband forgives her, she finds she is unable to attain an orgasm because of the way she previously mistreated her husband. I have treated many wives who complain of frigidity and who confess to guilt feelings because of the way they abuse their husbands.

Desexualizing the husband brings on autocastration in the form of frigidity.

If a woman wishes to gain and maintain sexual satisfaction throughout her marriage she must be careful not to desexualize her husband by castrating him via rejection, conversation or behavior. You can't mix his food with ground glass and expect to feel free of guilt. Guilt in turn will bring on self-hatred which in turn will result in *frigidity*.

Personality Incompatibility

Sexual compatibility and personality compatibility are interrelated. Better companionship during the day means better sex at night.

A woman is less apt to respond sexually to a husband who abuses her. Stekel repeated many times that love between a husband and wife constituted the greatest cure for their sexual maladjustments. There must be a harmony of souls to achieve the maximum sexual satisfaction. A wise husband will make it his business to treat his wife with kindness and understanding as he knows she is more apt to be sexually cooperative if she feels loved and wanted.

One of my patients told me that she had always been able to attain a vaginal orgasm during coitus until she learned from her husband's own admission that he had been unfaithful.

At the time she consulted me for advice regarding her estranged relationship to her husband she expressed her sentiments as follows:

"I don't want sexual intercourse with H—(her husband). I don't get anything out of it anymore—ever since he told me he had relations with L—(my girl friend). I used to be all right sexually. But I've been holding back, maybe to punish him. His kisses don't arouse me. He has his climax but I don't want to be bothered. I don't touch him any more. I used to love him. I get along with my husband after a fashion but I have absolutely no sex desire. I find myself refusing to have sex relations with him at times. When I do have intercourse, it's not pleasurable. I would just as soon that my husband wouldn't bother me sexually. Sex is repulsive to me now. I loved my husband but now I don't have any feeling for him. Maybe I shouldn't feel this way. It depresses me. Do you suppose it's why I have so many throbbing headaches?"

The above illustrates the "will to displeasure" theory which Stekel describes in his books on frigidity. The woman may submit to sex relations with her husband as a duty but she realizes that her husband cannot compel her to enjoy the act. In fact she deliberately "holds back," motivated even at the conscious level by a desire to punish him for his infidelity. Of course she fails to appreciate that this revenge motive behind her self-imposed frigidity brings harm to herself. Not getting a proper outlet for her pent-up sexual tension she develops what is known among psychiatrists as "conversion symptoms." The throbbing headaches symbolize her sexual dissatisfaction and unhappiness.

Women who develop this "will to displeasure" (a refusal to enjoy intercourse) are only spiting themselves. Sometimes the vindictiveness is unconscious. The wife goes through the motions of pretending that she is experiencing pleasure, but she complains that nothing happens—that she never reaches a climax. When she is confronted with the theory that she doesn't want to enjoy intercourse because of the way she feels toward her husband, she quickly denies it.

Frigidity in these cases serves as a weapon for many women—a means of expressing their hostility toward their husbands.

Psychotherapy attempts to expose the unconscious motivating factors behind their frigidity and reeducate them to the point of restoring their original sexual response to their husband's lovemaking.

A good sexual relationship is apt to exist when both husband and wife are fortunate enough to be endowed with a normal personality; when they exhibit evidence of being well-adjusted, and are adequately prepared to fulfill those obligations that constitute the foundation of a happy marriage. They are tolerant and understanding, know the meaning of love and were free of serious complexes prior to marriage.

I have found from experience that when the husband and wife are emotionally unsuited for each other, being opposite personality types, and are unfit for marriage by reason of emotional immaturity or premarital neurotic complexes, the sexual relationship is always a bad one.

A patient who complained of being frigid admitted to me that the only reason that she married her husband, whom she didn't love, was to get away from her unhappy parents. She had been exposed to constant quarrelling at home and had left to escape it. It was evident that she could not hope to respond to her husband's lovemaking as long as she reminded herself that she did not love him and engaged in constant bickering over trivialities. A maladjusted love life means a maladjusted sex life. Frigidity in one respect is a form of *selfishness*.

A couple recently consulted me because their personalities clashed to such an extent that it affected their sex life. They were completely opposite types. Jane was selfish and spoiled, aggressive and dominating. Jim, her husband, was passive, shy and inhibited. He complained that his wife was *frigid* and fulfilled her physical obligations only as a *duty*. She refused to cooperate by accepting treatment, stating that there was nothing wrong with her, that her husband was a clumsy lover and that a separation was the only answer. She obtained a divorce.

In the meantime, Jim was psycholanalyzed, became aware of his shortcomings, improved his personality and launched out on a new life for himself. He met a girl with a congenial personality, married her and is now completely happy. Because of the personality compatibility they have physical compatibility. Love is the cement that holds the bricks of *mind* and *body* together.

I have found that persons are sexually happy or unhappy according to their ability to give love and their capacity to receive love. I remind my patients that love must be earned, that love isn't just hugs and kisses. It is a condition of the mind, a sense of inner tranquility that communicates itself to others. The capacity for love is present in the soul of everyone. It is a feeling, a philosophy rather than a treasure-find. Love is to be found within ourselves.

7.

FRIGIDITY AND DREAM ANALYSIS

The unconscious causes of frigidity are often found in the patient's dreams. The interpretation of dreams enables a psychoanalyst to get at the root of the particular sexual neurosis quickly without having to subject his patient to an expensive or prolonged analysis.

For instance, one woman brought in the following dream:

"I was taking a bath. My husband was in the water with me. I felt I couldn't wash my sex parts until he went out. When he left, I had a terrific urge to masturbate by rubbing my clitoris with the wash rag."

The dream discloses a fixation of her sexuality to her

clitoris and a suspected *preference* for masturbation. It also conveys her guilt by wanting to be alone in order to masturbate.

The next dream is quite symbolic of frigidity.

"My husband and I were driving up a steep hill. I was driving at the time. When we got halfway up the hill, I felt I would never make it as the car began to lose power. My husband said to me, 'Why don't you shift into second?' When I tried, it wouldn't work and we finally stalled. I had to put the breaks on to keep from rolling down the hill."

The above dream signifies an attempt made to reach a simultaneous orgasm by getting to the top of the hill. Being unable to make it is symbolic of her inability to achieve a climax. The fact that she is driving the car is symbolic of her unconscious wish to assume the dominant role (clitoral aggression). The husband assumes the passive role by going along as a passenger.

In another dream she claims her husband was urinating on her and she became extremely angry. She cursed him because she was "so mad."

This would tend to reveal her sado-masochistic make-up. (Hostility toward her husband whom she thinks wishes to defile her, and at the same time it gratifies an unconscious masochistic wish to be humiliated at the hands of her husband—to be his sexual slave as it were.) This dream explains why some women remain married to a man who continually abuses them either sexually or in acts of physical violence.

Dreams such as the following are also typical of women who are frigid.

"We were invited to dinner and my husband kept telling me to hurry. Each time I thought I was ready, I had to run back into the house for something else I had forgotten. My husband told the hostess that I was to blame for being late and apologized. It made me mad when he said that I am always late."

"Being late" is symbolic of her inability to achieve an orgasm at the time her husband expects her to.

More evidence of clitoral sexuality can be found in this next dream:

"I was sleeping with my legs separated. My husband rubbed his knee against my clitoris. I got an orgasm."

A very significant dream involved her brother.

"My brother was trying to pry open a glass door with a screwdriver. The glass shattered. He turned to me with an affectionate gesture. Just then he heard a noise and was afraid of being caught and would have to go to jail. I awakened crying."

The above dream suggested the possibility of an early psychic trauma namely that her brother may have once attempted to rape her. This was confirmed by her associations with the dream. The screwdriver represented a penis symbol in the dream; the glass door symbolizing the vagina and the shattering of the glass as the act of defloration or breaking of the hymen. The guilt is evidenced by the fear of being caught.

She also adds that on one occasion her brother kissed her on the lips and she experienced a peculiar reaction.

So-called frustration dreams are common to many women who find it difficult to experience a coital orgasm. This next dream is symbolic of her attitude toward her orgasm incapacity.

"I was going to bake a cake for my husband but when I went to light the oven, it wouldn't light. I was disappointed and cried."

The oven, of course, represents her vagina which she wishes to warm up. Not being successful in lighting the oven signifies her sexual difficulties.

The latent homosexual component associated with her masturbation practice is further revealed in the next dream:

"I was searching for the ladies' toilet. I never found one. I experienced an orgasm by merely touching my clitoris."

The incest motif is seen in a dream which she describes as follows:

"I felt someone was in my room. He was almost transparent. He reached out and grabbed me by my breast. I made a noise like a small child. He looked more like my father."

In many cases of frigidity, psychoanalysts have often discovered that their patients were victims of these early psychic traumas wherein an alcoholic father or brother attempts to rape the patient during her adolescent years. In other instances they might not have been actually raped but the father or the patient's brother are careless and sometimes expose their sexual organs as to leave a lasting impression on them.

In another dream she quite obviously betrays her homosexual desires:

"I was sitting in a room with a woman friend. I was in such a position that my thighs were spread apart. The woman placed her hand on my sex parts and said 'Do it to me.' I then put my hand on her sex parts and had an orgasm as soon as I touched her. In the meantime, she had rubbed my clitoris."

In her associations to this dream she commented as follows:

"I once met a woman through my brother. She was a Lesbian. She tried to teach me to dance and said I was wonderful, lovely and attractive. She would press me close against her. It nauseated me. One time she very carefully ran her hand up my leg. My brother finally told me she was a 'queer.'"

The above case responded favorably to psychoanalytic treatment as her dreams clearly revealed the sexual conflicts that caused her to be frigid.

Another patient who had never attained a vaginal orgasm during coitus related the following dream:

"I was in a kitchen with a man. I have no idea who he was. He was playing with a small snake. It was about six inches long and marked "Rattler." The snake was wiggling and squirming. The man forced my hand on it and made me hold it in my hand. Of course I jerked away and dropped the snake. I screamed in my sleep but I did not awaken. He then placed it between two slices of bread and made a sandwich. He tried to make me eat it. At this point I fought back, screamed and awakened."

This dream reflects an actual experience when a man attempted to have her perform fellatio on him. The snake, of course, is a penis symbol. She has always had an aversion to touching the male organ and during intercourse with her husband she experienced no pleasure whatsoever.

In another dream this same fellatio fantasy appears:

"I was sucking on a long piece of candy. As I walked along a country road, a sticklike object reared up. I thought nothing of it for a while. Then it's head darted toward my face. It was a snake. I ran but it came after me. Then I realized that it smelled the candy. I threw the candy at it. It leapt into the air to catch it. The candy choked it. It writhed horribly and liquid sprayed from its mouth."

The liquid symbolically refers to the ejaculation of semen. She manifests anxiety in the following dream which indicates a preoccupation with death fantasies.

"I was in a rowboat in the middle of a lake. I noticed the boat leaked. It soon became full of water and started to sink. I became terrified, and cried for help. But no one was around to hear me. I began to drown. Everything turned black."

Her exhibitionistic impulses are portrayed in the next dream:

"I was under seven fountains of water. I was wet and

cold and had no clothes on. Someone handed me a towel which I put around my body. Some men came along and tried to lift the towel. Just then my mother and dad came."

The following dream definitely corroborates our previous conclusion that there existed an unconscious wish to perform fellatio which incidentally came to the surface when she stated that prior to marriage she harbored a fear of becoming pregnant. She preferred to satisfy her date, as she put it, "in ways other than intercourse."

"I dreamed I was out with a boy who worked where I did. We engaged in some light petting. Then he placed my hand on his penis which was stiff and hard. He asked me if I knew what that meant. I said, 'Yes.' Then he wanted me to place it in my mouth and succeeded in ejaculating a little bit in my mouth. I withdrew from him. He then had me masturbate him. This I did until the penis was no longer stiff and hard. I then went over to the ladies' room and washed the thick fluid off my hand and spit the stuff from my mouth. The spit had blood in it. He then took me in his arms and told me how sorry he was. He said that he thought that I was more used to such things and that I had been around a little more. He then kissed me and told me to remember that he would never harm me no matter what happened, never to be afraid of him. Then he left."

The fear of becoming pregnant is evidenced in the next dream:

"I was walking into a high building and entered an elevator. When I got out, I discovered I lost my purse. A man behind me had it but he wouldn't give it to me. He started to paw me and I pleaded with him not to. Then I found myself in a room with him. He made me sit down on his lap, straddling his knees. He placed his penis in my vagina. I could feel it was hard. Then there was a lot of moisture. He laughed and said he was going to force me to have a baby. I begged him to stop. I finally got away and when I got up water and a white fluid ran from me all over the red carpet. I washed my sex parts carefully with hot water and soap. The man had my purse and still wouldn't give it to me. Mother came and I was going up in the elevator with her. I was afraid the man would relate the story of what happened to my mother."

As previously indicated frigidity among some women represents the symptom consequence of unconscious guilt. It apparently is borne out in the next dream:

"I walked through the woods with a friend. He asked me if I would like a cigarette. After smoking most of it, I threw it away without putting it out. I later learned there was a forest fire in that area and felt extremely guilty.

"In the same dream, I found myself in a refrigerator plant trapped in a large icebox. I concluded God was punishing me for starting the fire."

Fire is a symbol of sex. The icebox is symbolic of frigidity as a punishment for sex guilt.

She brought in many other dreams in which she depicts her horror of snakes. Her *frigidity* was associated with premarital sex guilt, fear of pregnancy and of the male organ.

One patient who was quite resistive to treatment brought in several dreams which gave me a clue to some of the deeper, unconscious factors involved in her failure to respond to her husband's lovemaking.

For example, a number of her dreams revealed a strong latent homosexual component. Here is one of those dreams:

"I was alone and was wearing white cotton panties. I had a terrific urge to masturbate. I looked in the mirror and I could see I had two small testicles. I didn't have an orgasm while masturbating."

There are other dreams to indicate an unconscious wish to have been born a boy and to have possessed a penis (penis envy).

In another dream she has a penis and a wolf was biting it off (penis envy and castration anxiety).

Her homosexual cravings are revealed in the following dream:

"I was with two women. One of them was performing cunnilingus on me. The other looked on. I had an intensive orgasm. I said, 'It feels good.' They had a lot of lipstick on their lips."

The next dream contains fear and guilt as emotional factors which unconsciously influence a woman's sexual response.

"A terrific storm broke out. It rained and the streets were flooded. I found myself running in an open field and was afraid I would be struck by lightning. I prayed that God would save me."

Fear of God's punishment is indicative of guilt. Many women who for instance are aware of homosexual tendencies often experience considerable guilt and consequently suffer from various states of anxiety and panic.

In another dream her partner has a premature ejaculation.

"He started to make love to me. Just as he was putting his penis near my vagina he squirted all over my abdomen."

The following dreams were submitted by a married woman who was unable to attain a vaginal orgasm during coitus with her husband. Her frigidity was the result of an Electra Complex and guilt associated with the practice of a sexual aberration (flagellation).

This patient dreams that her breasts were giving off a watery secretion. This could be interpreted as an unconscious desire to have been born with a penis so that she could enjoy the act of ejaculating. Another time she dreamed of being spanked but was aroused in her sleep by the thought that this was wrong. Another dream of spanking is described as follows:

Dream 1. "I dreamed I was spanking my sister. She was grown-up and lying over my knees. Her slip was up and I was using my hand. I dreamed I could see her buttocks. They gave me a passionate feling."

The following dream suggests an incestuous element in so far as it pertains to her analyst and an old man, a father surrogate:

Dream 2. "I dreamed I was expecting a baby. There was

no pain. I dreamed that you (the analyst) were going to deliver the baby. I could see you. The baby was never born. There was an old man in the dream."

In her associations to this dream she states that she has thoughts of seeing her father in his long underwear. Her anxiety is further evidenced in dreams of falling off high buildings. The next dream is overtly incestuous in character.

Dream 3. "I dreamed a man was lying on top of me trying to have intercourse with me. I think it was my father. I recognized his face. I had a slip on."

In the following dream she develops a skin eruption which incapacitates her for sex relations with her husband. Frigid women often use illness as an excuse not to fulfill their physical obligations.

"I dreamed that my husband wanted to make love to me but I pushed him away because I had a contagious skin disease and didn't want him to get it."

A patient who had been raped by her father during early adolescence brought in the following significant dreams. It was apparent that her frigidity following her marriage to a man who reminded her of her father was traceable to her incestuous relations with her father.

Dream 1. "I had a horrible dream the other night. I had a feeling of suffocation as if they were closing in on me. I became frightened and started to climb out of bed."

The above reveals her feelings of guilt in the eyes of people or society. The suffocation is in keeping with her idea of self-punishment—the wish to die.

In the next dream the man symbolizes her father. It also reflects an annihilation in her unconscious mind of the incestuous relationship that occurred at the age of fifteen.

Dream 2. "I dreamed that a tramp was running after me. I was running out of a cellar trying to get away. He didn't catch up with me."

The tramp, of course, is another symbol of the father. His not catching up with her is wishful.

She also has dreams of falling from heights.

Her sense of guilt is disclosed in the following dream:

Dream 3. "I dreamed that I had thrown away my brassiere, and when the maid, an elderly woman, came to clean the trash box, she held it up between her two fingers and seemed to be saying something which I couldn't understand, but I had a terrible feeling of shame and guilt."

The elderly maid represents her mother. The throwing away of her brassiere symbolizes her desire to release herself of her sexual inhibitions.

The following dream is symbolic of the sexual trauma involving her father:

Dream 4. "I dreamed that I was with a man. I don't remember who, but he seemed to demand something from me. What, I don't know. My refusal made him very angry. He was holding both my hands and pushing me forward, but I kept holding back. Suddenly he had a razor blade in his hand and he threatened to cut my hands. While I looked on in terror he started to cut my flesh. I felt neither pain nor did I see any blood which surprised me, even as

I was trying to scream for help, although unable to make a sound."

Making demands represents her father desiring sex relations with her. The razor blade is a penis symbol and the cutting into the flesh symbolizes the penetration of the hymen. The fact that she suffered no pain and saw no blood suggests the possibility that she may have experienced masochistic pleasure in being raped against her will. Further evidence of this can be found in the fact that she wanted to scream but could not utter a sound.

The next dream is classical in the sense that it reveals the Oedipal relationship to her mother and father, and represents another echo-dream of the incestuous rape:

Dream 5. "My mother was looking in a box and said, 'Someone has been taking money from me.' I left to go into another room and I seemed to go through a bathroom where a man was washing a toy rubber doll. He had what appeared to be an ice pick through the doll's stomach, and as he squished the doll I could see the dirty water coming out of the doll. I thought that it was a funny way to wash it."

The mother looking into the box symbolizes looking into the vagina. Money being taken away from her represents the daughter's awareness that she has taken away from her mother the father's penis which rightfully should have been her mother's exclusive property. The ice pick is a phallic symbol. Puncturing the doll's stomach symbolizes her defloration by her father. The ice pick appears in the dream because it is a sharp instrument and is symbolic of the pain which she experienced during the penetration of the hymen. The dirty water coming out of the doll obviously symbolizes her father's ejaculation.

The resolution of this patient's guilt via catharsis and insight into the root cause of her frigidity enabled her to achieve vaginal orgasms for the first time in her married life.

8.

PREVENTION AND TREATMENT OF FRIGIDITY

The Role of Parents and Society

In the prevention of frigidity parents must be re-educated and advised not to instill in their daughters a sense of false modesty, fear, guilt or repugnance to sexuality or men. The sexual education of the daughter during adolescence should be the responsibility of the mother, who incidentally, should be well advised in sex matters. As we have learned, sex ignorance, misinformation and inhibitions are common causes of frigidity.

Parents and society are still hampered by old fears, old shames and old taboos. To quote Pastor Samuel E. Howie, "Taboos about sex have caused more unhappiness—including physical and mental suffering—than any other area of ignorance in the long life of the human race." We cannot afford to sit back and do nothing about the consequences of sex ignorance. Enlightenment in sexual matters means less frigidity and fewer divorces. Society fails to realize that sex incompatibility is responsible for four-fifths of all divorces, and that many illnesses among wives are due to sexual discord.

Fortunately women are gradually becoming emancipated from the cultural taboos and restraints imposed upon them by society. It is encouraging to expect less frigidity in the future as a result of this new freedom which women are enjoying. Justification for this encouragement can be found in the words of the French psychoanalyst, La Forge, who wrote: "It is a fact that women have only conquered the *right to experience orgasm* and also their freedom, in recent years, so that they must go through an immense emotional development within a very short time *which will probably wipe out the frigid middle-class type of woman* of the turn of the century, as well as the bigoted school ma'am and the pale-faced other-worldly 'ascetic.' Literature, which only a few years ago was subject to a strict censorship, as well as public opinion, of which it is an expression, is free and gaining more freedom still. The sexual problem, owing to the increasing influence of *psychoanalysis,* is being treated more objectively, and new discoveries are everywhere leading to enormous changes in the life of States as well as in the life of individuals."

Parents too must accept *their* responsibility in imparting

knowledge about sex to their children. They must be convinced that knowledge is power, that ignorance in matters of sex can lead their children into a maze of mental and physical ills.

Daughters must be taught to think right about sex. Men too, must be enlightened regarding adequate technique. The sex education of our youth is the only intelligent approach toward reducing the increasing divorce rate, the number of abortions (as high as a million a year), and diminishing the incidence of impotence and frigidity.

Parents must stress the fact that sex is related to a feeling of love for someone, that it is something happy and good to look forward to when their daughters get married someday.

The parent who wants a daughter to grow up sexually healthy will never instill any kind of fear in her. To give sex an association of fear or sin or disease in a daughter's mind is a destructive thing. With such an association, the growing daughter doesn't even get to the basically normal attitude toward sex, much less progress to the finer type of sex relationship in adulthood.

Even among the well educated and intelligent mothers, there is too often a reluctance to face the problem of educating their daughters in matters of sex. Mothers don't know when or how to start the education and often make the mistake of putting it off indefinitely. A wall of silence between mother and daughter makes it harder to discuss and deal with any problems that may come up when the daughter is older.

Unfortunately, many mothers are unfit to teach their daughters about sex because they have had no sex education themselves, or because they suffer from a sexual maladjustment of one kind or another.

Early in life the daughter is conditioned to grow up to be very much like her mother. Obviously, the mother's attitude toward sex will strongly influence that of the daughter. Mothers should check up on their own attitudes toward sex before passing them on to their daughters. The daughter can't be expected to adopt a normal attitude if the mother regards sex as something taboo or shameful.

Preparing For Marriage: Sex Education

Sex education is necessary in any preparation for a happy marriage. Books written by doctors dealing with various aspects of the subject are now available in bookstores and libraries. We have reached the point where educators are considering courses in sex hygiene as a regular part of school education. Some high schools and universities have already made sex hygiene part of the curriculum. A major factor in a successful marriage is an understanding of sex and how to achieve a healthy sex life.

It is never too soon to start learning. Start now. You will

become part of the modern trend for better understanding and better adjustment in matters of sex.

In preparing for marriage every girl should be made to realize the importance of adopting the right attitude toward sex. There would be *less frigidity* if more women would heed the words of the late clergyman, Dr. Peter Marshall, who wrote: "Next to hunger, the most powerful of human instincts is that of sex. You cannot escape from it, for you are made that way. It pulses in your blood, sings in your throat, and shines in your eyes. Sex will be either the nicest thing in your life—or it will be the nastiest—depending on whether you use it or abuse it. Only in nasty minds are there nasty thoughts about sex. There is nothing shameful about the sex urge."

Many other distinguished clergymen are coming to recognize the need for premarital sex education. It has been estimated, for example, that over fifty percent of those who go to a minister for counsel are troubled by some problem related to sex behavior.

The Rev. Russell L. Dicks of Duke University was one to realize the necessity of sex guidance as a major preparatory step toward a happy marriage, as evidenced by his statement: "I would consider it less a sin to give my blessing to a woman who had had excessive premarital sexual experience than to a girl entering marriage without premarital sexual instruction. The heartaches that will come to her and the unhappiness that will spring from the ignorance in which that marriage is conceived will echo down through generations. . . ."

A significant statement in keeping with this same trend of thinking came from Rev. Robert W. Burns, pastor of Peachtree Christian Church in Atlanta, Ga. He said: "Anyone who thinks there is anything *dirty* about *sex is not yet qualified for marriage.*"

Eric Northrup, authority in science and social psychology, in an article on Sex Education reports a case that involved a woman who went to her minister, shortly after her marriage, with the tearful confession that her marriage was a failure. She said, *"I am hopelessly frigid."* Northrup informs us that she had gone on the night before her wedding to her aged family doctor, who had listened to her fears with paternal indulgence, then disposed of the matter with the advice: "Now, now, don't worry. Mother Nature will take care of everything." It required several weeks before the minister could impress upon this woman that frigidity often is the result of early parental warnings that sex is "nasty" or painful. In this particular case the woman's mother had frightened her daughter, conveying the impression that marriage involved "painful submission" for women.

It is gratifying, to say the least, that pastors of various church denominations have finally awakened to the need for premarital counseling in sexual matters.

Preparing for Marriage: Premarital Medical Examination

Young women who are about to embark on marriage would be wise to undergo a thorough medical check-up to eliminate whatever physical conditions need to be corrected. A *healthy* bride is generally a *happy* bride. Health complaints detract from the romance of the honeymoon.

Chronic fatigue and a general rundown condition may act as predisposing factors in the development of frigidity. Proper tonics and adequate rest may be a necessary requirement in some instances to alleviate these symptoms. Menstrual disturbances should also be investigated by a gynecologist. I have found from experience that those patients who complain of menstrual difficulties are most apt to suffer from frigidity. They are also the ones who complain that intercourse is painful.

It is more intelligent to postpone the marriage until such time as chronic ailments have been treated with proper medication and the health of the couple is at its peak. It makes for a better start in marriage.

Impotence and frigidity are sexual disorders found more frequently among the weak and the sick, as well as the misinformed.

Preparing for Marriage: Surgical Defloration

To brides who have had no premarital experience or preparation, the honeymoon raises a spectre of fear and pain. While the bride has a fear of pain, her groom has the fear of hurting her, and between the two of them, they develop honeymoon anxiety. Usually, with a normal couple, this corrects itself in a week or two, but the situation sometimes results in unpleasant or even hostile conversations that do not belong on the honeymoon.

This situation can be avoided by *surgical defloration* (the artificial rupture of the hymen) followed by premarital dilatation of the vaginal introitus.

I had a patient at one time, a young girl, who needed a complete course in sex hygiene. During the course, in one talk, she was given information that was later to save her marriage. On her honeymoon, she found that she was totally unable to have relations with her husband. If she had been ignorant she might have gone into panic, and her husband might have misunderstood genuine, physical difficulty for virginal timidity.

The girl had learned in her course in sex hygiene, that occasionally a very resistive hymen requires surgical defloration. In these cases, a doctor is needed to anesthetize and incise the thickened hymen so that the prospective wife can start her married life comfortably. This bride went to a doctor in the town where she was honeymooning, and found that her difficulty was one that needed surgical correction.

She wrote me that the saving instructions in her course had enabled her to achieve a good adjustment with her husband, and prevented the shock and bad feeling that would have resulted if she had continued in ignorance.

Dr. Russel Jansen, a prominent gynecologist in Washington, D.C., concurred with me in the wisdom of having virgin brides undergo a premarital examination followed by an incision of the fibrous hymen and a dilation of the vaginal introitus. This procedure, of course, should be resorted to only with the consent of the prospective bridegroom and her parents. Many other gynecologists feel that this so-called anatomical preparation for the honeymoon would eliminate the pain that usually accompanies the "wedding night rape" and would make sex relations much more enjoyable.

In addition to this physical preparation, the bride-to-be should also be given some instruction on the role of sex in her marriage.

The Ideal Sexual Relationship: The Right Attitude

It is exceedingly important that a woman, particularly one suffering from frigidity, acquaint herself with what is regarded as ideal cohabitation.

In the first place she should give up this hush-hush attitude about sex and feel free to discuss the problem of adequate sex technique with her husband. She should accept sex as a physiological outlet—capable of influencing her physical and mental health. It is the only sensible and practical approach to the improvement of her sex relations. There is no excuse for a modern woman to become nervous and a health-neurotic because of being *sexually unsatisfied*.

Husbands must be made to understand that the ideal

sexual relationship means *mutual gratification*. If a husband is interested only in his own sexual gratification, his wife is bound to become *frigid*. If the wife feels it is her *duty* to give herself to her husband independent of her own needs and desires, she will soon invite the development of frigidity with each intercourse.

Both husband and wife should be kind and considerate, and regard sexual communion as something *beautiful*, not animalistic: a universal expression of love defined by Pfister, the famous Swiss psychoanalyst, as "a feeling of attraction and a sense of self-surrender arising out of a need and directed toward an object that offers hope of gratification."

The Ideal Sexual Relationship: Fore-Play

The love-play prior to actual intercourse is exceedingly important. It should produce sexual excitement in both partners. The breasts, particularly the nipples, can be caressed manually, digitally and orally. A normal woman *enjoys* having her husband fondle and kiss her breasts. Mammillary stimulation is one way in which he can arouse his wife's sexual desires. Local stimulation of the clitoris manually or orally is also essential.

Kissing various parts of the body, especially the erogenous areas, helps to prepare the wife for the enjoyment of the sex act. Fellatio and cunnilingus as preliminary forms of sexual excitation may be regarded as normal love-play technique provided there are no serious conflicts involved in their practice.

The late Dr. Abraham Brill, famous psychoanalyst, found that deviations from the normal were frequently encountered in the "intimate lives of otherwise normal people." He goes on to say: "We call them perversions only when they absolutely dominate the picture, that is, when they are fixed. Occasional indulgence in these acts does not stamp those practicing them as abnormal." Dr. Wolbarst expresses the opinion of many psychoanalysts today, when he states that "it can be demonstrated that many of the so-called perversions are often found as a normal constituent in the lives of normal individuals. Freud has said that 'probably there is no healthy person in whom there does not exist at some time or other, some kind of supplement to his normal sexual activity to which we should be justified in giving the name of perversity.' When we take into consideration the fact that the tendency to variation is inherent in the human race, savage or civilized, it may be regarded from the scientific viewpoint as coming within the category of the normal if they serve as contributive factors toward the stimulation and the higher satisfaction of the fundamental instinct for intercourse between the sexes and not as an end in themselves."

Saliva acts as a natural lubricant. The love-bite is also harmless if it is controlled in its expression. It appeals to certain women endowed with a passionate nature who find it very stimulating.

While the husband should be the predominant active partner, and initiate the lovemaking, the wife should at times assume an active role, so that the love relationship becomes a reciprocal one. Dr. Van de Velde states in his *Ideal Marriage*: "A certain feminine initiative and aggression brings a refreshing variety. Let her be the wooer sometimes, not always the wooed. She can be so while quite retaining her distinctive dignity and sweetness. This role of wooer can express her love in a very desirable way, and be intensely gratifying to the husband, who feels that he not only feels desire, but inspires it too."

The wife should remind herself that her husband is more apt to perform adequately if she indicates that she is in a receptive mood for sex relations. This she can do by taking the initiative occasionally to reach out and fondle his penis, caressing and kissing him in a passionate manner and resorting to whatever preliminary love-play she thinks or has discovered brings the most satisfactory results.

No wife need to apologize for expressing her natural desires for sex gratification. She should convince herself that the normal husband appreciates a wife who is "active" in lovemaking, who "teases" and "stimulates" him and who ultimately makes known physically via coital movements, etc., and verbally via expressions of ecstacy, her enjoyment of the entire sexual episode.

She can reaffirm her satisfaction in the course of the husband's after-play by telling him how happy he has made her.

This type of relationship exists among happy lovers. It is the desired goal which other couples should try to achieve remembering that it can be attained through sex enlightenment and practice or guidance from a competent psychiatrist if necessary.

The Ideal Sexual Relationship: The Act of Intercourse

The penis must be introduced into the vagina slowly only after there has been sufficient preliminary dalliance or fore-play to bring about a "sexual wetness" in the vagina. The to-and-fro strokes must be slow at first and followed by a crescendo of movements until both partners are ready for their respective orgasms. The husband must be careful not to cause his wife any discomfort or pain. He must not place his full weight upon her, impeding her from her own coital movements and thus making it exceedingly difficult for her to experience an orgasm.

It is best for the husband to kiss his wife during the act. Keeping the eyes closed enables both partners to concentrate and increases their chances of experiencing a simultaneous orgasm. The husband, in introducing his penis in the vagina for the first time must be careful not to ejaculate too quickly. He can train himself to move in and out of the vagina slowly and stopping to rest if he becomes too excited. He must also advise his wife to stop any movements on her part if he fears he is going to ejaculate prematurely. A deep breath, a moment or two of rest, a distracting thought will help him in controlling his ejaculation. After several miscellaneous to-and-fro strokes he should instruct his wife that he is now ready to give her an orgasm. This readiness is equivalent to runners lining up alongside of the starting line and waiting for the gun to go off for the start of the race.

If the husband resorts to the use of a condom, he should have had it on just before entering into this final phase of the act. It is best to have the contraceptive within arm's reach on a bedside table instead of interrupting the lovemaking by looking for it at the last minute. Such interruptions can seriously interfere with the sexual enjoyment.

Some husbands and wives have a signal system of letting each other know the moment they are having their orgasm.

The Ideal Sexual Relationship: Variations in Position

While there are any number of positions which ideal lovers may invent or discover to enhance their sexual pleasures, there are only a few which are most commonly resorted to. Changes in position have the advantage of making the act more enjoyable. It enables the couple to experience different types of sensations. Others find one position works better than another. The positions most described in sex books are:

1. The Man-Above Position.

2. The Woman-Above Position.

3. The Sitting Position (the man sits in a chair and the woman straddles him moving up and down or forward and backward on his penis).

4. The Side Position.

5. The Position From Behind.

The woman-above position affords many women greater freedom of action so that there is greater friction against the clitoris. The same holds true of the sitting position. Variety and experimentation are both healthful and proper. The husband should discuss with his wife the method or position which gives her the greatest sex pleasure and intensity of orgasm.

There is no rule that tells couples they should adhere to one classical position.

The Ideal Sexual Relationship: Frequency of Intercourse

As to the frequency of intercourse, most couples engage in sexual relations on the average of two or three times a week. Excessive coitus has a tendency to make many wives *frigid*. It is better to have sexual relations during more or less regular intervals. Having intercourse every night for a week followed by a period of abstinence lasting several months is not ideal technique.

Married couples should plan mutually for a time of intercourse harmonious to both. They should agree in advance on their time for lovemaking, so there will be no misunderstandings and resentment.

Giving in to a husband at all times is not being intelligent. It is not good for either husband or wife and makes sex less desirable. If a husband has been brought up in the old fashioned tradition that a wife should have relations whenever he requires it of her, she should explain to him in a nice way that she cannot give him a good response unless she is ready for him.

A husband and wife should be candid about their desire for each other. If they consistently select a time when the mood is mutual, the relationship will be happier and more enjoyable for both.

Many wives experience a greater sexual urge a few days before and a few days after their menstrual period.

Compromise means better adjustment for both. Each has to make concessions to the other's needs. In order for each to learn the other's preferences they must be honest with each other.

There is an element of adaptation in the sex relationship that is like adapting to tastes in food. If a husband never tells his wife what he prefers in a meal, she may go on serving him things that disagree with him for the rest of their lives together. If a wife never tells her husband of her special preferences, in a restaurant, he may order the exact opposite of what she wants and spoil the evening for her.

In sexual response, there should be frank requests for what is needed for the best harmony. It might be for a little more time, a different position. Many married people make the mistake of being too shy in the bedroom, to tell their preferences and go on for years sighing inwardly over failure to respond to the partner's lovemaking. They need to be reminded that they have only one life, and time is slipping away.

An ideal sex relationship in marriage is not only a joy while you have it, it is like an investment fund that is returned with interest when you most need it.

The Ideal Sexual Relationship: After-Play

During the after-play there must not be an abrupt withdrawal of the penis, but a slow retreat as it were. The husband should continue to be tender and affectionate even though he has reached his climax.

Women like to be loved and embraced after the act has been completed. When a satisfied husband abruptly falls asleep, his wife interprets this as a sign of his infantilism (the baby that has been fed and falls asleep). It makes her feel he was only interested in his being gratified. The man who kisses his wife's breasts, embraces her and engages in a conversation of a lovable nature finds that his wife is far more congenial and responsive. It gives her a feeling of security—of being wanted not only for sex' sake but because of being *loved*. Few men realize the need to make a woman feel loved even though she has achieved her orgasm.

Psychotherapy

With few exceptions there are no frigid women. There are only those who are *sexually ignorant* and men who are *inexperienced* and selfish. It is a matter of sexual reeducation, and eliminating the mental block responsible for the lack of response via psychotherapy.

Prudish attitudes act as barriers to sex enjoyment. The husband's technique must be improved, if this is necessary. Sometimes a change of position accomplishes results. Couples need to find that method of technique which is capable of making the sex act pleasurable. Psychotherapy must succeed in eliminating fears. Much of the success in treatment however, depends upon the husband's ability to cooperate by being gentle, kind and a skillful performer.

The wife who masturbates in preference to intercourse must abandon her autoerotic practices if she hopes to achieve gratification from coitus.

There must be frank discussions between husband and wife if the sexual difficulty is to be solved. They must tell each other their special needs in order to make sex more enjoyable. Sexual experimentation often produces encouraging results.

Aphrodisiacs or sexual stimulants may heighten the sex desire but they seldom cure the condition.

Approximately 90 percent of all frigidity cases are caused by *psychological* factors.

Psychotherapy today is considered the best specific cure for frigidity. It is capable of uprooting preexisting guilt complexes, removing neurotic taboos, exposing feigned morality as an obstacle to sex enjoyment, and getting at the deep-rooted complexes and fixations which may be retraced to early childhood that are very often the unconscious causes of frigidity. In other words, the underlying neurosis must be resolved before frigidity, the symptom-consequence of the neurosis, disappears.

A woman must be made to understand that the elimination of frigidity with the help of a psychotherapist will mean better physical and mental health, which in turn will influence her personality to advantage.

One patient who had been cured of frigidity (resulting from premarital prudishness) began experiencing orgasms for the first time during intercourse, much to the delight of her husband.

In describing her sexual responses she wrote the following:

"When I had my first orgasm, I had a feeling of well-being, self-assurance and intense pleasure of being with my husband. I had a vivid awareness of the world, its beauty and an exhilarated feeling of wanting to enjoy life. I felt alive. I even felt I had become prettier and more attractive after having had an orgasm. I've looked in a mirror and noticed a changed expression on my face—one of happiness and satisfaction."

It should be of comfort to thousands of sexually unsatisfied women to know that frigidity can be cured by psychotherapy.

9.

FEMALE HOMOSEXUALITY

Women with Souls of Men

Psychotherapists have found that many cases of *frigidity* are intimately related with the problem of *female homosexuality*. According to Havelock Ellis, there are twice as many lesbians as male homosexuals. Morris L. Ernst and David Loth claim "The Kinsey figures on woman can be anticipated to show an even greater incidence of homosexuality among women." Dr. Shailer Upton Lawton and Jules Archer, authors of *Sex Without Fear*, estimate that from five percent to eight percent of American women are lesbians, involving between three and five million women.

Female sexual inversion is therefore becoming an increasingly important problem. It is believed by some that women are becoming rapidly defeminized as a result of their overdesire for emancipation, and that this "psychic masculinization" of modern women is causing them to become frigid. One writer for example, states: "Women are modifying their position in the world. In innumerable ways the status of women has changed during the past century, alike legally, economically, politically and socially. The process is still going on. We cannot be surprised that it should spread to the sexual sphere."

The popularity of masculine-tailored clothes is only one of many evidences of the defeminization trend among our present day female society. The presence of the smoking habit is considered by psychiatrists as a form of "psychic masculinity." It may be only a coincidence, but a significant one, that the lesbians I have interviewed were for the large part excessive smokers.

In the field of sports women have taken up exhibitionistic wrestling, softball, basketball, golf, tennis and have entered many of the competitive athletic Olympic events. The modern generation, in other words, has tended to favor muscle development with less attention to cosmetics, a type of vitality that doesn't rub off one's cheeks, greater emphasis on careers and less on domestic activities, such as cooking, sewing, etc.

A few sexologists fear that this defeminization trend may seriously effect the sexual happiness of modern women. They claim it will more than likely influence the susceptibility of many women to a homosexual way of thinking and living.

An American correspondent in one of Havelock Ellis' volumes of Sex Studies wrote:

"I believe that sexual inversion is increasing among Americans—both men and women—and the obvious reasons are: first the growing independence of the women, their lessening need for marriage; secondly the nervous strain that business competition has brought upon the whole nation. In a word the rapidly increasing masculinity in women and the unhealthy nervous systems of the men, offer the ideal factor for the production of sexual inversion in their children."

There are others who feel that this new freedom which women are enjoying serves as fertile soil for the seeds of sexual inversion referred to as "the fashionable vice of the modern age." It is not surprising in the face of all the changes that are taking place that many lonesome as well as pleasure-seeking women prefer to replace heterosexuality with an exploitation of sexuality amongst themselves.

This fight for sexual independence, however, is contrary to a woman's basic needs. At best it represents a pseudo-aggressiveness or masculinity. Women unconsciously prefer to fulfill their maternal role and to be loved by a man.

As Bauer, author of *Woman And Love* so aptly expressed it: "Freedom for women means freedom to love. But we cannot go against Nature. Woman is intended for reproduction; she has been appointed to take an active part in the reproduction of the race by pregnancy and child-birth. And while these laws of Nature remain every attempt at emancipation is futile."

There are two types of masculine women. 1. The kind who are aggressive, normally independent, emotionally mature, who may or may not be athletically inclined or mannish in physical appearance, who may be quite active in career activities but who assume the role of a woman when it comes to a love relationship with a member of the opposite sex. They enjoy sex relations with their husbands, respect them and make good wives and good mothers. Although they may be regarded as masculine in many ways, they are predominantly a woman at heart. 2. The other type—the neurotically masculine women—are those who are dominating, over-aggressive, wear the pants as it were, whose career becomes the most important thing in their lives, who manifest reactions of *frigidity* or *orgasm-incapacity* during sex relations with their husbands, who unconsciously deny the role of being a woman, regret having been born a female, and are regarded by psychologists as falling in the masculine-protest category. It is this latter group who have become defeminized who are unaware of the cause of their sex-unhappiness in marriage. They are emotionally and sexually frustrated and prefer pseudo-masculinity to feminity.

Their renunciation of womanhood is unconscious. This same rejection of feminity exists among many lesbians. This inability of modern women to accept their own femininity can sometimes be traced to early childhood according to Dr. William Niederland. He informs us, for example, that some girls manifest an early desire to be a boy and take pride in being referred to as a "tomboy." Emotional conflicts develop when a mother reminds her daughter that she is a girl and should behave like one. Dr. Niederland cites the case of a 32 year old woman who complained of a band of pressure about her head, chronic fatigue and inability to sleep. Because of an absence of any organic condition he suspected that these symptoms were psychogenic in origin. His patient had been brought up in a very strict home environment by parents who were extremely prudish. The patient recalls how her parents made her understand that they wanted a boy and that she had been a disappointment to them. This frustration made her aggressive and she fought against being a woman. As Dr. Niederland tells us "although she married at 26, she could not reconcile herself to the idea. She was angry at her husband's desire for marital relations, found no pleasure in them, and resented him for relegating her to an inferior position as his woman slave."

The above applies to many wives who are unable to explain why they do not experience pleasure during sex relations with their husbands.

Dr. Niederland describes another patient who admitted to him that she "detested men." She was 44, single and atractive. She firmly convinced herself that all men were selfish and could not be trusted. She turned down several marriage proposals. In business she proved quite successful. Her mother was responsible for her aversion toward men. She filled her daughter's mind with tales of the "evil nature of men" inferring that all they thought about was sex. This naturally made the daughter fear going out on dates and she associated courtship with something that was obscene and lewd. As a result she cheated herself out of every opportunity that might have led to a happy marriage and instead became an embittered lonely spinster.

Defeminization doesn't always lead to sexual repression, as cited above. Neurotic masculinity in women may give rise to promiscuity (an unconscious repudiation of femininity—a desire to enjoy the same sexual freedom as the male sex).

The masculinity-complex found in many women as a result of defeminization trends in modern society must be dealt with as it is responsible for the development of homosexual patterns of thinking. As Dr. Niederland advises, women who have a masculinity-complex should be made to recognize it in themselves and be taught that if unchecked it can lead to serious difficulties. Lesbianism is only one of several consequences. Through psychoanalysis a woman can achieve such an awareness and voluntarily renounce the wish for masculinity, preferring instead the role of a woman, thus strengthening such feminine qualities as warmth, understanding, love and tenderness.

I have encountered many woman patients who were unable to experience sexual satisfaction with their husbands because of a strong latent homosexual component. Their latent homosexuality is manifested by a strong will to dominate the opposite sex, and a running away from femininity, marriage and motherhood. Their inability to be receptive, accepting the role of a woman in sex relations, makes them frigid. Frigidity, in these instances, represents a masked symptom of their lesbianism.

The rejection of the male sexually is common to women involved in overt homosexuality. Many women turn to female homosexuality because of being either sex starved or unable to achieve sex satisfaction with the opposite sex. They experience greater sexual stimulation and excitement from intimacies with their own sex.

Not all women inverts possess masculine features. There are lesbians who are mannish and those who are feminine. The masculine type walks like a man, wears low-heeled shoes, prefers to wear tailored suits, has her hair cut short and possesses a masculine body structure. She admires women who are feminine and beautiful. She is athletically inclined and often seeks out a type of occupation which offers her an outlet for masculine aggressivity.

The feminine type has an absence of masculine traits and is least suspected of having homosexual tendencies. In this group may be found wives who appear well-adjusted in marriage, as well as unmarried women who are seen frequently in the company of men. Often times a woman is unable to experience an orgasm during coitus because unconsciously she prefers sexual intimacy with her own sex.

Stekel describes the case of a thirty-nine year old woman

who at the age of fifteen was raped by a man whom she never saw again. At the age of eighteen after having had sex relations with several men, she met a woman with whom she became sexually intimate. This woman fondled her breasts and practiced cunnilingus on her. She found it so enjoyable that thereafter she was only able to achieve an orgasm through homosexual practices. She lived with her woman friend for eight years enjoying mutual sexual gratification.

A patient who complained of orgasm-incapacity during coitus revealed the following account of how she became involved in homosexuality:

"My homosexual experience began when I answered a 'lady to share' apartment advertisement in the newspaper. My friend, Miss A, age thirty, was very sympathetic and a kind woman who was responsible for initiating me into the mysteries of lesbian love. Our homosexual relations consisted of mutual masturbation and cunnilingus which lasted approximately five months. I decided to move to New York City, where I lived in Greenwich Village for two years with four different girls. Two of them were artists. One was a writer and the other a hostess in a hotel restaurant. I carried on sexual love affairs with these girls until one day I met a wealthy elderly lady, rather masculine in appearance, cultured and sympathetic to the highest degree. Through her influence I learned to appreciate music, art and good reading. She asked me to live with her and we practiced cunnilingus together. One winter, following an attack of pneumonia, she died. I was prostrated with grief. I learned from her attorney that she had mentioned me in her will and had left me a considerable amount of money. I have recently met a man who has been courting me for the past eight months. He wants to marry me. Although I have a great deal of respect for him, I feel sexually frigid towards him and have been unable to reach a sexual climax whenever he has sexual relations with me. I feel that my nerves are on edge and am in desperate need of advice."

It is not uncommon in any large organization, for example, where women congregate to the exclusion of the male sex, that homosexual friendships occasionally develop. Seductions take place in prison, boarding schools, clubs, branches of the military service or wherever women are closely associated with one another. Often times maids are seduced into lesbian practices by their mistresses.

A student at a private boarding school was seduced homosexually by her roommate. They slept in twin beds. One night during a lightning storm, the roommate appeared to be frightened and asked if she could crawl into her bed for protection and comfort. During the night she made advances and soon engaged her partner in homosexual practices.

I agree in part with Professor Moll when he states that the only person who can be seduced is the one who is capable of being seduced. But Moll tends to overlook the so-called involuntary seductions which involves the latent homosexual component and degrees of susceptibility.

As far back as 1886, Professor Benjamin Tarnowsky showed that homosexuality and other aberrations of the sexual instinct were sometimes caused by seduction. Kautzner substantiated that viewpoint by emphasizing the important role which seduction plays in sexual inversion.

The prevalence of homosexual seductions can be accounted for by the fact that more women have repressed lesbian tendencies than they are aware of.

In one instance, a patient told me she was initiated into what she refers to as the "inner circle" made up of lesbians who enjoy doing things in a "wild bohemian way." They all became sexually intimate with one another in the midst of frequent jealousy reactions.

She relates one of her homosexual experiences as follows: "I developed a particular crush for H—. She fascinated me probably because she was the first person with whom I had homosexual relations. She virtually seduced me. One summer evening while walking together, she told me how much she loved me and invited me to go to her apartment. As soon as we entered, she closed the door, rushed toward me and gave me a 'French kiss.' I slept with her that night. We engaged in mutual fondling of each other's sex parts until we were both satisfied. I remember that I particularly enjoyed fondling and kissing her breasts which were well-developed in contrast to my own. I became jealous of her and consequently the relationship did not last very long."

The above patient claims she had had sex relations with

several men but was never able to achieve a vaginal orgasm during coitus. Following intercourse she would masturbate her clitoris with her finger and experienced what she called a "weak climax" after much effort.

As a rule innocent women are more apt to be seduced into lesbian activities. This is because a young girl when kissed by a woman friend thinks nothing of it. Women kiss and embrace each other quite freely in public. Women are more apt to exchange gifts and develop a mutual warmth of feeling for each other. The experienced lesbian may proceed slowly and invites the innocent one to spend the night with her. She begins by embracing her and finally she winds up with cunnilingus or tribadic gratifications. Even at this stage the girl that is seduced may think there is nothing wrong with her love for the woman friend, that it is pure and noble and is swept away by the intensive pleasure she achieves during the lovemaking. Her curiosity prompts her to reciprocate. She may even experiment by taking the active role. The dissillusionment sets in when she discovers that to the experienced lesbian partner, it is just a matter of another affair. When she becomes interested in some other woman the jealousy becomes acute and complications ensue. Or vice versa when the girl who has been seduced shows interest in another girl, the experienced one becomes jealous, possessive and literally guards her like a bird in a gilded cage.

When an innocent girl abandons herself to the voluptuous lovemaking of the experienced lesbian she gives little

FEMALE HOMOSEXUALITY

if any thought to the consequences. The same girl ultimately becomes adept at seducing others like herself who are willing to venture into the ways of lesbian love. It is this cycle or chain of seductions that accounts for the increasing incidence of lesbianism in our midst.

A young girl in her early twenties was referred to me by her physician who diagnosed her case as one of "nervous indigestion." Her chief complaint was nausea and vomiting. Nothing seemed to allay her symptoms. When she began to get progressively worse, he came to the conclusion that the vomiting must in some way be associated with some deep unresolved emotional conflict. He was correct, for she had been seduced by an experienced lesbian and developed a severe case of anxiety neurosis afterwards as a result of her feelings of guilt. She was very religious and reproached herself for allowing the episode to happen. The nausea and vomiting of course symbolized how she felt about the experience. The symptoms served as a disguised defense reaction against her latent homosexual tendencies. We know, for example, that strong reactions of disgust may be diagnostic of an inner secret attraction for that which our conscious self rebels against. It was brought out in the case of Alice.

Alice was invited to spend the weekend with a married friend whose husband had been away on business. She accepted, never suspecting anything of a sexual nature would take place. They enjoyed a home-cooked dinner and the hostess succeeded in getting Alice to drink more wine than she could handle, which put her in a carefree jovial mood. They became playful and in bed began to tickle each other in an innocent way. During the night Alice claimed her hostess told her she was frigid but had never admitted it to her husband. Shortly after the hostess put out the light, she began to kiss Alice and rolled on top of her in the position of "Soixante-neuf." Alice found herself imitating her hostess in the performance of cunnilingus to the point of experiencing a climax and concluded that her hostess had also achieved a climax. Following their simultaneous orgasms, they fell asleep.

In the morning Alice discovered that her pulse was rapid and following breakfast had to go to the bathroom to vomit. She felt extremely self-conscious. The thought of what she did the night before, had nauseated her. She was unable to look her hostess in the eye and told her she was very sorry for what happened. The two of them never saw each other again.

This was the only homosexual experience Alice ever had. She never confessed the experience to anyone and tried to forget it but she found that her vomiting became worse and she was unable to continue at her job.

She made a rapid recovery following psychotherapy. Psychoanalysis enabled her to unburden her soul as it were and she was given to understand what psychological factors entered into the development of her sexual neurosis. She was completely innocent and didn't know that such a phenomenon as lesbianism ever existed. At any rate she claimed she became that much wiser by virtue of her experience and developed a healthy attitude toward love, sex and marriage.

In another case, a girl who had been seduced into her initial lesbian experience submitted some rather significant data relative to her sexual background. While the following information is fragmentary, it does throw some light on her psychological make-up.

As a young girl she was regarded throughout her community as a tomboy.

"When I was a kid I wanted to be a boy up to the age of 13. My brother was my companion. If we played games I wanted to be the father instead of playing the role of mother. I'd put on my brother's clothes. I'd imagine myself in the movies playing the role of the male lover. I admired good looking girls."

Thus we see early evidence of her transvestite tendencies —the desire to wear her brother's clothes and the masculine drive—the wish to adopt the male role. There was a renunciation of her sex at an early age. She became preoccupied with masculine activities (psychic hermaphroditism).

Her first psychic trauma occurred when she was five. She engaged in sex play with a boy of her own age. Her mother caught her in the act and threatened that if it ever happened again God would make her die. She developed a fear of God ever since which is still present to some degree.

Her emotional insecurity as a child was enhanced by family discord. Her parents separated for a while and then effected a reconciliation. She remembers them quarrelling and bickering frequently. They said mean things to each other.

She showed a definite leaning toward the father and blamed her mother for constantly nagging him. This father-identification became transferred on to her brother whom she imitated and admired.

She began to masturbate around the age of 16 and felt very guilty trying in vain to stop the habit. She thought it would cause her some kind of physical injury.

She denies ever having had intercourse with anyone.

Her dreams tend to betray her homosexual craving which at the conscious level are repressed. In one dream she is giving a girl friend a "soul kiss." In another she is massaging a woman's buttocks.

Regarding her attitude toward lesbianism she states: "It is a handicap. You are marked a 'pervert'—an unfortunate child of nature. I can't understand why anyone would care or choose to be a homosexual if they were honest with themselves in evaluating the worth of it."

Some writers believe that once a wife is seduced into the ways of lesbian love, she becomes completely indifferent to her husband in order to live in a man-wife relationship with a lesbian partner. Dr. Mehta in his book, *Scientific Curiosities Of Sex Life*, quotes Dr. La Forrest Potter of New York who believes from his own experience of tribades that "once a woman is seduced by one, it is almost impossible for any man, husband or lover to win back his wife or sweetheart from the fascinating toils of these perverts. No man stands any chance against an active Sapphist once she has properly seduced a woman with her wiles."

Clinical experience tends to dispute the validity of such a sweeping generalization. It may be true in some instances, but there are many women who have been seduced homosexually and who prefer heterosexual relations and wives whose husbands are expert lovers and who are gratified completely by their husbands but who allowed themselves to experience a lesbian relationship out of sheer curiosity.

Several years ago an attorney informed me that whenever he had occasion to be away for a week-end his wife would ask a close woman friend to spend the night with her. Each time they met, they would imbibe in alcoholic beverages as a preliminary to their sexual indulgences which consisted of tribadic practices and occasional cunnilingus. A quarrel arose one day and the jealous partner in a spell of vindictiveness confessed to the attorney that his wife was a lesbian and had accosted her sexually whenever she was under the influence of alcohol.

Another of my patients, a young woman in her early thirties, consulted me because she claimed she was promiscuous and wanted to know how she could control herself. She stated that she had led a life of dissipation for the past eight years, drank to excess, and had no plans for the future. She married at the age of twenty-four and discovered she was *frigid*. Her husband divorced her because she had been unfaithful to him. Following her divorce she began to drink and has had sexual relations with innumerable men. The case is interesting from the standpoint of showing the interrelationship between *frigidity*, promiscuity, prostitution and latent homosexuality. She denied having lesbian tendencies but admitted that on numerous occasions, only under the influence of alcohol, did she engage in sexual intimacies with members of her own sex. Actually her promiscuity represented a flight from homosexuality. She struggled to repress her homosexual cravings but whenever she became intoxicated she found herself uninhibited, would make advances to some woman that attracted her, indulge in various forms of mutual masturbation and develop an alcoholic amnesia or at least a vague memory of what took place the night before.

One evening however, Daisy (the patient) remembered having met a girl at a tavern and spent several hours at her table drinking beer. She learned in the course of her conversation that her newly acquired friend, a woman of middle years, rather buxom, was a professional prostitute. Nevertheless, this older woman decided to accompany Daisy home in a taxi thinking that she was too intoxicated to return home alone. En route Daisy started to fondle the woman's breasts, kissed her on the mouth and in the matter of a few minutes began performing cunnilingus on her companion. The older woman who had also been drinking, but was less intoxicated tried to resist at first but later abandoned herself to Daisy's passionate lovemaking. The driver of the taxi according to Daisy's story looked back to see what was going on when he heard groanings. The driver proceeded to take a different route and finally parked on a lonely road. The evening ended with the three of them indulging in various types of sexual gratification. The older woman brought Daisy home and the two of them never saw each other again.

On another occasion during an alcoholic spree, she was approached by a lesbian who brought her to her apartment. She has a faint memory that she asked her lesbian friend to spank her on her buttocks while she masturbated herself by manipulating her clitoris. She saw this particular girl several times afterwards and claims her friend broke up the relationship complaining that spanking did not appeal to her.

Daisy then decided to go "straight" as she put it promising herself she was strictly heterosexual. She became a professional prostitute for a while in the sense that she insisted that her male friends pay her a given price before she would submit to them. She learned to smoke marijhuana cigarettes. Her fear of being arrested made her give up prostitution.

Despite her life dissipation she manifested some willingness to be helped. She was more neurotic than psychopathic as she suffered from a deep sense of guilt, cried and felt remorseful whenever she drank to excess. Psychopathic women are rather callous, seldom display feelings of guilt and remorse and manifest no desire to seek psychiatric treatment.

This girl came from a very handicapped background. Her brother seduced her during adolescence. Both parents drank to excess. She ran away from home while still in her teens and never had anyone to show any real affection for her. She made two attempts at suicide during moments of despair.

Her sex life showed a preponderance of heterosexual experiences. The homosexual repressions gave way only under the influence of alcohol. Her latent homosexuality represented the need for maternal affection which she was deprived of as a child.

She availed herself of a series of psychotherapy sessions, developed insight for the first time as to the causes of her promiscuity and addiction to alcohol and decided to move to a southern state to live with an aunt.

Her case is also significant because her life-history revealed the extent to which she was subjected to psychic traumata. She attributes her maladjustment to the fact that she has always been lonely—never had anyone sympathize with her—or give her a feeling of belonging. She was always selfconscious although she had no reason to be as she made a fairly good appearance, spoke intelligently and had no physical handicaps of any kind. Her childhood was characterized by considerable sexual precocity. A girl friend taught her to masturbate and she masturbated to excess throughout her life. She claims she is attracted in a non-sexual way to women of the "motherly" type which can be construed as evidence of an unconscious mother-fixation, the nucleus of her latent homosexuality and *frigidity*.

While many women prefer to remain homosexual, there are many others who seek the help of a psychiatrist in order to make a good heterosexual adjustment. These women feel a sincere anguish because of their inability to enjoy a normal sexual relationship. They search eagerly for a happy marriage and family life.

There is hope for these women. Homosexuality, like frigidity, is curable via psychoanalysis and psychotherapy provided of course, that there exists a genuine willingness to be cured.

Bisexual Conflicts

Between the sexes there are found various gradations of feminine men and masculine women. We not only possess male and female physical characteristics, but psychologically we manifest a blending of the emotional qualities of both sexes.

There is some degree of homosexuality, latent or overt, in all women. In our sexual development the homosexual component (the preference for our own sex) becomes sublimated in the form of friendships and nonsexual activities. As we grow to maturity heterosexuality finds expression in the form of an attraction to the opposite sex. As the attraction for the opposite sex increases, the homosexual component becomes normally repressed. However, in some instances this repression of the homosexual component is not successful and the individual finds herself a victim of bisexual conflicts. She notices that she is attracted to both sexes equally, feels guilty about inviting an intimacy with her own sex and complains of not achieving complete satisfaction with the opposite sex. Psychiatrists have discovered that frigidity is often the symptom-consequence of this bisexual struggle within the woman.

A case came to my attention of a young woman in her early twenties who had experimented by becoming intimate with several men only to discover that she was unable to attain an orgasm during sex relations with them. She also became intimate sexually with two of her women friends with whom she practiced mutual masturbation. During adolescence she was shy and experienced strong feelings of inferiority. She never received any sex education from her parents and had learned whatever little she knew about sex from her friends. Psychotherapy succeeded in resolving her bisexual conflict which was responsible for her frigidity. She had been unable successfully to repress her homosexual inclinations and harbored strong feelings of guilt following each homosexual indulgence.

The following case involves a married woman whose frigidity was traced to bisexual conflicts in her premarital life as evidenced by her fragmentary account of her sex life:

"My mother turned me against sex. She made me believe sex was wrong, wicked and disastrous.

"When I grew up I met a friend (a school teacher) who was beautiful and brilliant. Everyone liked her. She was the answer to all of my wishes. I worshipped her. We slept together and spent all our free time together. We spent vacations together. At night she would touch my vagina and cuddle me. I did not like the direct touch but overlooked it. She asked me to touch her in like manner. I did so to please her. I never heard of perversions at that time. She apparently got a thrill from my touching her. I got nothing out of it but did not object to our actions because I loved her and she gave me the cuddling I was hungry for. It never occurred to me that it was wrong. After seeing it in a different light, I rather felt she took advantage of me. I see her only occasionally now but I still love her. She married the principal of a high school."

The susceptibility to a homosexual friendship is indicative of an unconscious craving for "mother love."

Patient continued: "I later turned to men. I had no desire for marriage but enjoyed the attention and petting which usually resulted in sexual affairs. I never wanted it but always gave in rather than hurt the men's feelings. This must have gone on with five or six different persons. I always had a great sense of guilt. When I married I discovered I could not experience an orgasm from intercourse. I began to realize there was something wrong."

Guilt associated with some past homosexual activity is capable of making many married women frigid.

Another case involved a young attractive woman in her early thirties who never married and had an extraordinary ability to make both men and women fall in love with her. Although she was unable to become satisfied sexually during intercourse with a man, she did enjoy orgasms whenever cunnilingus was performed on her either by a man or woman. She drank to excess, developed numerous psychosomatic ailments and sought psychoanalysis because she felt she might commit suicide as a result of her "many dissipations," to use her own expression.

Her analysis disclosed a definite Electra Complex (a father fixation). She related how her parents had slept in separate bedrooms as long as she can remember. Her orgasm-incapacity during coitus was traced psychoanalytically to an incestuous attachment she had for her father—a common factor in the psychosexual make-up of many bisexual women.

10.

THE MENOPAUSE

Problems of the Middle-Aged: The Slackening of Sexual Desire

Menopause or the "Climacteric" may be defined as the period in a woman's life when her reproductive capacity ceases. It is commonly referred to as "the change of life" and is characterized by a gradual cessation of menstruation. The onset of menopause varies with different women and may come on anytime between the ages of forty and fifty-five, being influenced by climate, mode of life, illnesses, heredity and constitutional factors.

Many women, depending upon their temperament, suffer from a host of psychosomatic ailments during this period to the extent that many obscure ills are attributed to the menopause. These health complaints (nervousness, dizzy spells, hot flashes, fatigue, irritability, insomnia, headaches, backaches, etc.) represent the culmination of frustrations arising directly or indirectly from frigidity. It is a fallacy that menopause brings with it a slackening of sexual desire.

Dr. Edward Podolsky in his book *Sex Practice in Later Years* quotes a doctor who expressed his views regarding menopause as follows:

"It is imperative that the woman learn more about all physical aspects of the advent of menopause. She must learn that her sexual desires last long beyond this period. She must become aware that the attraction she holds for the male can continue long after the menopause, if she will continue to care for herself in terms of physical and mental health. Once she realizes that many women at fifty or sixty are far more attractive than their younger sisters, and equally as passionate, she will not mourn the arrival of menopause; thereby eliminating much of the mental and emotional suffering which too often accompanies it."

Numerous women look forward to the time when they will no longer be troubled by their menstrual periods with their discomfort and inconvenience. They anticipate the time when the constant possibility of pregnancy no longer threatens them. But when the menopause is over, they get no joy from their new freedom, for like the men, they fear the diminuation of sex desire which marks them as being in the declining years. They feel that they have become undesirable to their husbands, that their mates will seek fairer, younger women. They, therefore, begin to preen their feathers, they don brighter clothes, they haunt the beauty shops, they take a refresher course in dancing, they catch up on current events—like the inmates of the harem, they wisely try to hold their mates. Or they may belong to that frigid group of women who grow slack; they stuff themselves with food and add layers of fat, they grow careless in dress and grooming, they have no interest beyond their homes, their grandchildren, bridge and the movies. Suddenly they wake up to find that younger, more attractive women have stolen their husbands from them. They grow bitter over the hand Fate has dealt them, not realizing how they have been cheating themselves.

It has been said that the first five years of married life make or unmake the harmony of the marriage. Middle age is almost as critical in the preservation of marriage. It is not uncommon to read of a marriage breaking up after enduring for twenty-five or even forty-five years. A fair share of the blame can be laid to abatement of sexual love. Some wives feel that sexual activity is designed merely for procreation and the happiness of parenthood, not for the gratification of the sex urge which does not cease when childbearing is over. The frigidity in which these women falsely pride themselves usually indicates a neurosis. Nature deliberately puts an end to child-bearing when the body has grown too old for perfect fertility, but Nature has not abated sexual desire except in intensity. It remains a tie between the woman and her mate.

I encounter a number of middle-aged couples each year

who come to me seeking advice as to what they can do to save their marriage. Invariably I find that they have ceased having sex relations or they engage in sexual intercourse so infrequently that their sex life is practically nil. Some women actually believe that sexual intercourse is injurious during the menopause.

One husband told me that his wife would keep repeating that he was too old for "that kind of nonsense," implying that sex desire dies with one's youth. He had passed his fifty-second birthday and was in fine physical condition. His wife, on the other hand, had been ailing for a number of years. Her physician had told her that her nervousness and spells of depression were caused by her change of life. She became more and more preoccupied with neurotic feelings of ill health. Her husband referred to her as a "hypochondriac" who enjoyed poor health. Whenever he approached her sexually, she rejected him, stating that she had lost all desire for sex relations now that she was going through her menopause. I informed her that menopause is not synonymous with the death of one's sex life, that any loss of sex desire at her age (forty-eight) was self-induced, and that her health complaints were neurotic in origin. She was cooperative and resumed relations with her husband, proving to herself that menopause was not the cause of her frigidity or indifference to sex.

It cannot be sufficiently emphasized that sexual life does not cease during menopause. Sexual pleasure is possible for a considerable number of years following.

There are other women who experience an intensification of sexual desire during the menopause. This creates a problem for the husband who feels threatened by a premature loss of virility. Generally speaking, psychiatric guidance is all that is necessary to assure such a husband that he can continue to function as an adequate lover and that there is no cause for anxiety relative to his wife's increased desire for sex. Sexual vigor is influenced by the mental attitude toward sexuality.

Those women who during menopause indulge in sexual excesses, becoming promiscuous and unfaithful, generally suffer from frigidity caused by their hysterical fear of growing old prematurely. They are often attracted to younger men. Husbands often seek professional advice, particularly when they become victims of wives who become indiscreet during this so-called "dangerous age."

Problems of the Middle-Aged: The Neurotic Spinster

It is difficult to convince the unmarried older woman that her failure to successfully sublimate her sexual energy accounts for her aches, pains and unhappiness. While the psychoanalyst cannot prescribe sex gratification as he would a tonic, he can explain to such sex-starved women that the repression of the sexual drive can be converted at the unconscious level into physical symptoms. I have found from experience that giving spinsters a lecture course in mental and sexual hygiene usually yields favorable results. They develop insight for the first time into the origin of their neurotic complaints. Many of them utilize their newly acquired knowledge to advantage and realize that one is never too old for romance and love. Incidentally it has been estimated, based on the ratio of women to men, that there are over 7,500,000 females in the United States who will never get husbands.

Many of these unmarried women are gainfully employed. They fear the older years because they know it may mean enforced retirement and they therefore go through the menopause without the fuss and claim for sympathy demanded by married women; they conceal their badge of departed girlhood. They put on a brave front, attempt to look younger than their years. They never give up the hope that someday romance will come to them, but most of all, they hope to hold their jobs. Some find ways of sublimating their sexual energy by becoming interested in clubs, philanthropic organizations or perhaps take to golf or other not too strenuous sports. Others settle down to lives of "little old ladies" and, in this particular manner, live in the present and in the past.

Problems of the Middle-Aged: The Repressed Widow

One hundred and seventy-six thousand more men than women die every year which makes the problem of widowhood an important one. In many instances the sexually repressed widow feels compelled to remain loyal to the memory of her deceased husband. She may become not only indifferent to any thought of remarriage, but may lose interest in everything. This combination of sexual repression, a loss of interest in all activities and a living in the past, all contribute to a state of chronic depression common to women in their middle years. Women need not consider themselves less attractive during their menopausal years. The beauty of a woman, whether married, a spinster or a widow, is often to be found in her personality—her attitude toward life, love and the pursuit of happiness.

Rather than allow herself to develop feelings of self-pity she must learn to convert her pent-up sexual tension into constructive activity. She should cultivate new friends, develop a hobby, and attempt to create for herself an entirely new pattern of living.

Sex and Love after Fifty

Frigidity is an *attitude*. One need *not* grow *colder* as they grow *older*. There are many couples past fifty who find satisfaction in sexual intercourse until the age of 65 or even 70. Love keeps the embers of the original romantic relationship forever burning. This love is embodied in a sharing of mutual interest, an exchange of kindnesses with the growing years as a means of gaining emotional satisfaction. The kiss, an embrace, a kind word means more with approaching senescence.

As Skolsky said, "Years are the artificialities of the calendar makers. If the spirit is young, the years are not even remembered. If the spirit remains young, one can sing a song of youth as at eighteen—but at eighty it will have more meaning."

Growing old is also a matter of attitude, not of arteries. We keep young by keeping our thoughts young. The longevity of sex and love is dependent upon our ability to keep our spirit young. By this we do not mean a return to the silly gaiety of youth nor to youthful dress and play. Nothing is quite so ridiculous as an aged person aping the young, a parody of youth. What is meant is that if we keep our interest in the progress of the world, if our education continues to grow, if we haven't lost our sense of humor, if we do not overevaluate ourselves and our own ideas nor underevaluate others and their opinions, then we do not grow old.

We are—

> "As young as our faith
> As old as our doubt;
> As young as our self-confidence,
> As old as our fears;
> As young as our hopes,
> As old as our despair."

The best way to cheat age is to learn to control our disabling emotions for the maintenance of a happy mental disposition upon which youth largely depends. Our goal is not merely a longer life but a richer, happier one. After all, there is not much point in lingering on in a vale of tears and tribulations. Unless the later years can be filled with zest, interest and meaning they are scarcely worth the effort required to keep the dull embers of life from extinction. Who cares to live unless one *can* live?

INDEX

Adultery, 25-28
Alcoholism, and sexual frustration, 28-31
Alcoholism, as a cause of frigidity, 30-31
Alcoholism, as a personality maladjustment, 33-34

Brill, Dr. Abraham, 178
Burns, Rev. Robert W., 173

Castration mechanism, 145-49

Davis, Dr. Katherine, 19
Divorce, cause of, 13-14
Don Juanism, 34-35
Dream Analysis, relation of to frigidity, 154-67

"Electra Complex," 118-19, 137, 163, 210
Ernst, Morris L., 188

Female Homosexuality. See Homosexuality.
Freud, Sigmund, 24

Frigidity, and dream analysis, 154-67
Frigidity, causes of, 17, 100-153
Frigidity, definition of, 15
Frigidity, prevention and treatment of, 168-87
Frigidity, types of, 83-99

Gambling, as a personality maladjustment, 36-37

Homosexuality, 77, 188-210
Howie, Pastor Samuel E., 168

Infidelity, and sex incompatibility, 25-28

Jansen, Dr. Russel, 175
Jealousy, 35-36

Kinsey Report, 13, 101, 188

Lesbian. *See* Homosexuality.
Libido, 127
Loth, David, 188

McPartland, Dr. John, 85
Marriage failures, cause of, 13
Masochism, 155
Masturbation, 77-79, 124-27
Menstruation, 71-72
Menopause, 72, 211-15
"Messalina Complex," 89

Narcissism, 87, 96-97, 127-28
Niederland, Dr. William, 192

Northrup, Eric, 173
Neurotic Husband, handling of, 44-60
Neuroticism, in relation to marriage, 38-39
Nymphomania, 89

Orgasm, 74-82

Penis-Envy, 116-118
Podolsky, Dr. Edward, 212
Potter, Dr. La Forrest, 202-03
Promiscuity, 128-130
Prudishness, 103-07
Psychic Traumas, 107-10

Sadism, 155
Sex, right attitude towards, 17-22, 168-71, 176-77
Sex Education, 171-73
Sex Complexes, 37-38
Sex Guilt, 110-16
Sex Ignorance, 103-07
Sexual Aberrations, 131-37
Sexual Organs, male, 61-66
Sexual Organs, female, 67-71
Sexual Technique, 43-44
Stekel, Wilhelm, 24, 149, 150, 194-95

Tarnowsky, Benjamin, 197
Terman, Dr. Lewis, 85

Vaginismus, 102-03